Bits
of
Ourselves

Bits
of
Ourselves

Women's Experiences With Cancer

Introduction by Clarice Dukeminier, M.D.

Illustrations by Cindy Davis

Vanessapress • Publishers
Fairbanks, Alaska

First Edition
ISBN: 0-940055-00-7

This book has been published by the volunteer Vanessapress Editorial Board, comprised of Liz Biesiot, April Crosby, Marybeth Harder, Mayo Murray, Marcia Nye, Sally Yarie, Wanda Zimmerman.

Typeset by Spirit Mountain Press.
Printed by Braun-Brumfield, Inc.

Cover: "At Home" by Marybeth Harder. Cover and book design by Marybeth Harder.

Foreword

"When someone in your family gets cancer, everyone in your family needs help," reads a recent American Cancer Society advertisement. So do your friends and everyone else who knows about the cancer as each tries to integrate that knowledge and as each faces a creeping sense of helplessness. We wonder what we can do. But there is a great deal that can be done for the sick, for their families, and for their friends.

During the six months that my mother was ill with liver cancer, the local Cancer Society and the Hospice organization called offering help. Those calls ceased when they realized that our family had mustered a great many resources to offer Mom. There were friends who sent regular cards, those who brought books, those who sent plants, and those who called each week at an appointed time. Some concentrated on trying to keep my father occupied, while others took care of me and my brothers and sister. Some friends ran errands, some provided transportation, and others brought food. There was so much appropriate help that my family wondered if someone was orchestrating the effort. One neighbor left a casserole, a meatloaf, a huge pot of chili or soup, or some other almost-prepared dinner at the door every three or four days for nearly four months. The doorbell would ring and, when answered, only the food remained. "Heat 'n' Eat came again," we'd say.

The idea for this volume developed when two of us who were Vanessapress Editorial Board members realized we had kept journals during the time we experienced cancer . . . in ourselves or in loved ones. Each of us had permitted a few friends to read the journals, and had received encouragement to publish our writings about cancer so that others might learn from our experiences.

Wondering if others from Alaskan communities had written about personal experience with cancer, Vanessapress issued a statewide press release explaining a potential book and requesting manuscripts. The resulting book, a compilation of eighteen pieces, makes an interesting and sometimes compelling anthology about how people cope with life-threatening illness. The pieces are educational, varied, depressing, moving, and at times inspirational. The volume is published with the hope that, through sharing such experiences, others facing similar illnesses will find alternative coping mechanisms, perhaps some friends, and perhaps some help.

Some of the writings in this book tell of the bonding that can happen when families or friends face fear. Others of the pieces are intensely introverted and personal. Still others reflect the solace sought from God or other sources of understanding and meaning. Vanessapress decided to publish this volume, our third, as an educational and emotional support effort for those dealing with cancer in themselves or in family or friends. We hope that many men and women will be able to identify with at least some of the pieces. The variety is offered to speak to as many readers as possible, since serious illness, like rain, falls on everyone.

April E. Crosby
Vanessapress Editorial Board

Contents

Introduction

In an age of explosive growth in numbers of books and journals and a painful awareness of the limited time available to read only a small percentage of publications, I have nevertheless encouraged Vanessapress to add this book to the world's library. There is a need for the kind of sharing expressed here. I would guess that every adult has a close friend or family member with the diagnosis/challenge of cancer. If we, as a civilized society, seek to aid the afflicted, it is imperative that we share the pain and understand the process of adaptation and healing — or death. The voices in the contributions contained in this anthology give us a variety of levels of understanding and of literary achievement, but they are all very human attempts to understand the meaning of life when a perceived threat of death — or impairment of the quality of life — presents itself.

Through a curious quirk in history and science, we can blame medical achievements for the increase in the modern-day incidence of cancer. For truly, if antibiotics had not been developed to cure infections, if all the techniques of anesthesia and surgery had not been developed to treat accident victims, and if modern obstetric techniques had not been developed to reduce maternal and neonatal mortality, people simply would not live long enough to develop cancer. (While most cancers affect mature adults, there are, of course, cancers that affect young people and children.) Another predominant factor that exposes us all to cancer is the increasing amount of agents in the environment that can produce cancer. Probably the most significant known agent at this time is tobacco. Lung cancer, which is related to tobacco usage, has long been the most common malignancy of men, while breast cancer has been the most common malignancy of women. Now, for the first year ever, the incidence of lung cancer among women of some geographic areas surpasses that of breast cancer. Lung cancer is now almost completely avoidable by refraining from exposure to tobacco. The 1986 Chernobyl disaster points to another environmental danger — as if we had not learned enough from the explosions at Hiroshima and Nagasaki about the long-term effects on cancer rates from exposure to radiation.

As a physician, I welcome this anthology as an aid to patients and to their family members to help cope with the challenge of a cancer diagnosis. One might think that, as an obstetrician, I am involved only with the joy of a safe entry into this world. The truth is, as a gynecologist and as a fellow human, I am just as concerned with the entire span of life and its meaning until it culminates in, let us hope, a graceful exit.

These contributions provide windows through which we can peep — windows that provide views of the experiences of others that will enable us to expand our own feelings and understandings into a connection with them and with each other. It is this network of shared feelings that gives us strength.

Clarice Dukeminier, M.D.

Bits
of
Ourselves

Human Sacrifices

Donna Mack

We try to strike
a bargain with the Gods.
Bits of ourselves,
for time.

We show our bloodless wares
on stainless trays
A breast ? A patch of skin?
A womb?

Before she died,
My mother said
She'd give anything
To stay alive.

A Year with Cancer: Journal Excerpts

BJ Webb

November 21, 1982   *Fairbanks, Alaska*

I'm 34 years old, I crave chocolate, and I have the whitest, ugliest pimples I've seen since puberty.

My life went on tilt a few days ago.

First I noticed a lump in my breast. I thought it was a bruise. But it never changed color and slowly, steadily grew. It's not going to go away.

I went to see Dr. Roth. He sent me to Dr. Borden. They want a mammogram as soon as possible. But the machine is broken down, waiting for parts — typical Fairbanks! — so that won't be until Tuesday afternoon. Then there's a biopsy. I wish it could all be done already. I was so tired last night I went to bed at 7:00.

This is undermining me so badly. Why? It's not something that marks a visible X on my lifespan, something that takes away arms, legs or sight. It's only a stupid boob, so small no one will notice it's gone. But the idea of not being able to look normal in a swimsuit, teeshirt, even bra, is appalling. Not a week ago I thought I might be ready for a close relationship. Now it's possible I could lose some of the equipment to lure with.

Lord that hurts. I want to be held and loved and cherished; yes, I want somebody to take care of me for awhile. I need to lean on someone. It's so hard to stand alone, much less walk or run.

Who knows? Maybe this will just be a close call to

make me quit joking about my flat chest. A flat chest is better than none.

November 23, 1982   First mammogram

There's a picture stamped in front of my eyes that I'll never forget: me sitting in that little room at the hospital, and that machine with its single arm wandering out to maul boobs, and me in my slacks and that silly flowered smock that opened in the front.

The technician got me maneuvered into the machine's claw once and then hurried out to check the film. Bingo! The machine wasn't working. This is Tuesday. The soonest they can get me in — because they're waiting for parts — is next Monday. *If* the parts are here. I can't wait that long; tomorrow I'm going to try that place downtown. Otherwise I'll gain ten pounds or turn into an alcoholic or both and can afford neither.

Only a few days ago this was still something I could ignore; now it permeates my whole life and, I'm afraid, controls part of it. That's ridiculous. It's a thing. It has no consciousness. Therefore I should control it. After all, it's a small inhabiter of my body — not vice versa.

All I want is to know the nature of the thing growing in my breast, and then I want to know the best way to be rid of it. I want it out! Gone! Out, out damn spot!

November 24, 1982   After testing

Touchstone. I've been thinking that word for a few days. Last night after I went to bed I remembered it. I got up and pulled out my giant dictionary and looked it up.

It said touchstone is a black gritty stone once used as a

testing base for metals. They would strike the metal against it and know its content purity by the mark it left.

Am I the touchstone? Or am I a lump of metal beaten against some rock? Instead of marks, I leave blood and tears.

December 8, 1982   *Day before surgery*

I have only a few hours left now until surgery. I have only that long to remain whole and complete, a woman still.

Yes, it does feel that way. It's not an arm or leg that I face losing; it's just one breast; it's not even a very big one. But with it goes my confidence, my ability to express my sensuality, much of my hope for full and happy relationships in the future.

I wonder if other women react this way: the greatest fear in my mind is not the cancer. Perhaps I'm just not allowing myself to look at it. Tomorrow, this beast and I must come face to face.

This afternoon, in Dr. Carroll's office, that beast and I had a nice long introduction — but he never came close enough into the light for me to see. I know his outline, I can feel the coldness and evil seeping out of his presence. Tomorrow I will know his name and we will deal with each other. Tomorrow I can't deny him; he will have devoured a part of me.

I may always wear the scars, inside and out, of this battle. But I will fight it. I will win.

December 17, 1982 12:35 A.M.

Another late-night vigil. For some reason I've put off writing until now, my second night at home, with "Heartlight" on the tape player. The day after the surgery, in the hospital, I tried to write, but my hand was swollen and I couldn't hold the pen.

I told my sister this evening that my perspective has changed on everything. On those long nights in the hospital, I clearly came face to face with that beast I talked about before.

He was waiting for me there in the darkness, stinking of fears and death. His teeth showed when he smiled at me and they already dripped with blood. His claws ripped at me and I heard him laugh — and darkness began to close around me.

From somewhere in me I recognized a stronger strength, one patiently and quietly waiting to be summoned. It was like a cool white light, a kindling for a powerful conflagration that bellowed, physically flowed through me as soon as I clothed it in thought.

Some day, in another world, I'll know this source of strength and power better. Now, I know that it is there and that it works. I believe it is that to which Bah'u'llah summons us in *The Hidden Words* to look within ourselves to find.

Since that night I've been on a upwinging spiral. Yes, it's true that there is fear. But its substance is mushy and insubstantial, easily exorcised. I get so excited about living. Friendships have such greater meaning. Obviously I'm pleased to be able to continue them, but could it also be that I found that many of them go deeper than I thought, with bonds of loving embraces and silken ropes?

Since that night with the beast, every medical test I've had has given me a clean slate. But I have a year of

chemotherapy, six weeks of radiation, because the cancer
got into my lymph system. Such a greedy monster.

I know that I may have to face this beast again. I hope
that I can still know the source of that white light and that
unlimited power.

Somewhere in a surgeon's
steel sterile tray they dropped
my chopped breast

probably threw it out, then,
with yesterday's corned beef hash

I thought they took
my heart too
for a while I felt
a hole where my
core used to be

but I found out
my heart is attached
quite firmly
very nicely

thank you

not crushed against
any touchstone
still soundly counting out
the rhythm of my life

January 6, 1983

I start the long chemotherapy tomorrow. I'm a little nervous about it. But I also have a clinical interest; it will frankly be interesting to see exactly what it is, how it works. Do other people have that outside-their-own-body interest, looking at themselves as though they were mechanical habitats? My body is the robot inside which I live.

And then there are the times when I can't disassociate things like the loss of a breast from the things most integral to me.

Late that night

John checked Nancy into the hospital tonight; she has surgery at 8:00 in the morning. John told me some pretty scary details: when I asked if they knew anything yet, he said it looked pretty bad.

For three years she's been fighting stomach cancer; it looks like her fight is slowing down. When no one else was around, there at the Baha'i Feast, he told me that they gave her one to two years. For a couple of minutes I couldn't do anything but hold him and cry. She won't let anyone really close to her, but maybe I can be a friend and lighten her load. Not by myself; with God's help. I'm learning that living with cancer is something you can't really do by yourself. It's ironic that you have to face the big truths alone but that you need support to do it.

Tonight I went to see Nancy at the hospital. I said things in front of her I'm not sure other people do. I have the right to say the word "cancer" in front of her because I have it too. I can talk about chemotherapy because I have that, too. I can talk about the day-to-day dealing with cancer because I have to do it. I, too, have looked at death. They haven't put a limit on my life, but I have no guarantee they won't.

Nancy commented that I always seem so "up," so I told her a little about the night I spent in the hospital facing down the beast. I told her I loved her. She seemed glad I was there.

January 7, 1983

After work tomorrow I'll see Nancy in the hospital. Her surgery was this morning; I talked to John and he said it was very bad. He said she didn't want him to talk about it, so he didn't; but apparently she doesn't have long to live.

My hands paused over the keys when I typed that; I can't accept it. I want to love her back into living. She can do it, but she has to come out of that shell. She can do it, can't she? Oh God, can I reach her? Should I try? Life attracts life; it's an immutable law of nature. I love Nancy; I don't know her well, but I've seen glimpses of such a beautiful lady in there.

I'll be there if she wants to talk. I'll encourage her to open up. Maybe she'll trust me. Lord, help me. I'm afraid. I'm alone. Crying again.

January 8, 1983   Late at night

Chemotherapy/magic. I'm applying the half-full/half-empty glass theory to this: it can be unpleasant or it can be magic, depending on how I look at it. It's no big deal. Nothing much happens: he gives me a bunch of incredibly expensive pills and some intravenous stuff. I don't like getting poked with needles but I'll get used to it.

They want a blood count before every treatment. If it's too low, they'll give me a transfusion or skip a treatment. I remember before the surgery Dr. Carroll asked me if I had a weak stomach or a strong stomach. I answered strong, thinking of the chili powder and jalepenos I lavish into my cooking. I may have inadvertently done myself a favor; I either baked the lining of my stomach or burned out all the nerve endings. I don't think I'll have any trouble with the treatments' making me sick.

In the waiting room I watched other people. There's a difference from those in an eye clinic, say, or a general practitioner's office. People in other offices are more casual, full of plans for tonight's supper or the needlework pattern they're busily stabbing.

In Dr. Carroll's office there are never as many waiting because the appointments are more spaced out. They know each one takes longer. The topic is usually the same: discussion and understanding are as much a part of the treatment as the pills and needles. Those who wait for Dr. Carroll's attention all battle the same beast; cancer. We have all learned its name too well. We know its clawmarks across our lives and bodies, its touch intimate as a lover's. None do needlework in the waiting room; none idly scan magazines; there is little idle chatter. There is also no self-pity. There are people who smile, and their smiles are quiet, self-lit, genuine. They know the coldness of the touch of death which has taught them the incredible warmth of life's embrace. Each one seems to have a light in the eyes that speaks of life; having come so close to losing it, they now revel in it, exude it. Those who don't give up gain even more life. Gene Kingrea, her face marked with the scars of her own battle, told me I could never drive down a street again without seeing it. I have a greater awareness now, a desire to watch and touch and see and smell and feel.

January 11, 1983

Sometimes I get weary thinking "cancer" and associating it with me. "What, me, cancer? Of course not!" I think it's because all the things I (like most people) associate with cancer are the dark and ugly things. And I'm very obviously alive and functioning — not just functioning, but *alive*. Medically I know that I have cancer; realistically, even if it's still there, it's on its way out. I feel that I have it defeated, with the help of people who love me and send me their prayers and surround me with their thoughts like favorite blankets and chatty letters. Life, how beautiful you are! Will I ever be able to look at a newborn babe and not weep? I doubt it.

January 16, 1983

It's hard to pick up a pen tonight. The evening has been rough. I've been unbelieveably short-tempered. If I could make Vicki go away, I would; she's just a dog, she can't help it, but she's driving me crazy. I trip over her once an hour, she stinks, she poops all over the sidewalk, I just want her to go away.

I talked to the folks on the phone today. Mom thinks I'm so strong and brave. Jesus Christ. Tonight I feel deserted, abandoned, forgotten. I miss — need, fear — male attention. Just when I'm looking bloated. Lovely, just what I need. I'm blossoming into a miniature beluga in the middle of this. Won't I be cute when my hair falls out too? Just like a plump pale pig.

I'm facing one of my most deadly dragons, the quiet sneaky kind that languishes back there in the shadows, producing malodorous sulphur and grinning to himself. Thinks he's so damn smart. Well, fella, it may take me a little longer to get to you, but I will. Looking at you I find your weakness. And since you're merely a spawn of the recesses of my own mind, you have no substance. I, your creator, have strength. I wish you gone.

Good lord, I feel almost relaxed again. Yes, still alone, but not deserted anymore. Maybe I'm getting better at handling cardboard swords; they can be quite efficient at slicing dragons. Cardboard is so much sharper than mist.

February 12, 1983

Just scratched my head and got a hair under my fingernail. Great. In the mornings I notice the drain in the shower is full of hair. Mine.

It's been two months since surgery, living with the beast. Oh, yes, he still rears his salivating jawed head and roars at me; sometimes he still sneaks up behind and nips my flanks. And then there are the times, even more subtle and painful, when he appears behind an opening door with that evil death's-head grin. Five times a day, suddenly reminded. It still hurts! Perhaps it always will.

Suddenly I feel very tired, like I got zapped with Flash Gordon's ray gun, or somebody twisted off my big toe and all the white warm energy just ran out in a diminishing puddle on the carpet.

February 28, 1983

Today Robin told me Nancy has four weeks to two months to live. I took a nose dive; I'm not over it. I have to admit that it's not just losing Nancy. I'm afraid.

April 19, 1983

Last week I found out my thyroid is too low. That explains my weight increase, my tiredness and coldness — synthroid should put me back on track again.

So tired of being fat and tired. Tired. I don't want to put up with it. Robin showed me pictures of her wedding last Friday — I looked awful. Bloated. Thin hair. I look so different from me! I'm still in there, but I sure look different on the outside. Like a beached beluga. I move like a whale, too. My joints hurt.

April 25, 1983

The muse malingered in my head. She didn't get up for several mornings in a row, finally rolled out midafternoon with bad breath and tangled hair and an incredibly bad attitude. I'd say to her, "I need to write now," and she'd say, "Go to hell." Then she'd closet herself in the bedroom with another package of M&Ms and a diet pop (one justifies the other) and brood over a trashy novel. She didn't come out at all for several weeks. The bedroom started smelling of stale thought and unlaundered emotions, the kind of mental filth that backs up on itself and dies in its own squalid inertia. They don't have a vaccine for inertia.

Potential and kinetic; plus and minus; hot and cold. One quality has no meaning, no measure, without its opposite. Pain is how you know you're happy; I want to scream in agony, I want to shriek with happiness. A time of extremes and excesses.

I wonder if I'll stabilize; I don't want to. I want to go on knowing the brilliance of sun in my eyes, the sharp cutting edge of the cold, the surge of electricity in my stomach when someone touches me. I want to always know the craziness of Sunday afternoon drives the first day it's really warm, the coziness of evenings in the livingroom in front of the wood stove.

And I want to know the sharing of these things with a man who knows them too. My mating instincts are going wild. I look for him in every male face I see, in every man walking across the street or buying groceries. I read faces, body language, nuances of speech, clothes. I haven't found him yet. Maybe he doesn't exist; maybe he is an impossible dream. I just keep looking into faces, looking for the unsaid things inadvertently revealed, hoping that soon I'll find the right things, the right motives.

How can I have cancer? God, I didn't ask for this. Did I use the wrong code or something? You have to help me. I'm so tired of the drugs, the treatments, the exhaustion, the explanations. I just want to live.

Sometimes I'm almost overcome with the impossibilities. I get up in the morning and — every single day — have to reacquaint myself with that horror when I climb into the shower. Could a man really get used to looking at that every day when I haven't? My logic tells me that for me it's much harder, that women are always tougher on themselves in these situations than anyone else. But my eyes still see the scar, ugly deformity where a breast should be.

Now look what you did to me, muse. You dredged up all the slime and let me wallow in it. Damn you anyway.

May 17, 1983

Robin and I may go to visit Nancy on Saturday. What do you say to a woman who's dying? What would I want said to me?

I stop and stare at these pages; the lines blur together. The things that cause my pen to stop moving are hurtful. God, sometimes I still find it hard to believe I have cancer. It permeates my whole life. It's not a novelty anymore; the newness wore off a long time ago, and I don't want to play this game any more. No wonder people die who can't accept it; it affects the whole body and attitude.

Being ordinary, being regular, being normal, would be wonderful. I don't want to have cancer, I don't want that round-eyed spectre following me the rest of my life, tapping me on the shoulder with its long bony finger. Natalie has spoken of me a couple of times as being "chosen." Perhaps she's right; it scares the hell out of me. Somebody hold me up.

May 25, 1983

Monday we — the local Baha'is — planted a rosebush in Bicentennial Park for the day of prayer for the Iranian Baha'is. Nancy was there — in the car, too weak to get out. John told me she wanted to talk to me. I sat with her a few minutes. She told me I could go sit in their yard if I wanted, over noon hour; she acted like she wanted me to be around. I told her I'd take her up on that. After work I bought her a lounging gown. I wanted her to have something pretty and to know I was thinking of her.

It was hard for me to go to her. She looks so different. She's incredibly gaunt and shrunken; her skin is wrinkled where her flesh used to be. I have to admit it: when I see her, I think that I could be there one day. All I know is that it won't be now, not for awhile yet.

June 5, 1983

Today was the Feast of Light at my house. Last night at midnight Nancy died. I don't think it an accident that she left this world on a feast day — this particular feast, always my favorite. John came tonight; I figured he would. He said there was no longer any reason to stay home. He seems very relaxed and calm. I'm worried about how he'll be when the funeral's over.

You hear knocking
open the door
nobody's there

The sound of
one fist pounding
one hand clapping
one heart pulsing
one soul singing

is like a mirror
image of itself
over and over
into infinity
repeating rhythms

unto, into itself
like a circle
constant

It doesn't need us
to survive
it shares itself
anyhow

Wait I have to
go there's
someone at the door

June 9, 1983

Tuesday was Nancy's funeral. If all funerals were like hers, people wouldn't dread going to them. It was full of music and happy memories related by her brother, full of prayers and readings reminding us that her residence now is joyful. In fact, sitting there wondering if I'd be able to hang onto myself, I felt tiny bubbles start rising in my middle. They grew steadily, surrounding me until I felt I was about to burst from intense joy. I swear I could have glowed in the dark! Maybe it was a gift from Nancy, a quiet message. I had really dreaded going to her funeral; in fact, I stayed home in bed Monday, bracing myself. Now that it's over I realize — again — that the reality of death is not so fearsome.

September 2, 1983

For a year now I've joked about being a nun; I answer the phone at my house, "Convent." But I'm not kidding any more: dead furnace, no money and lots of bills, no food in the kitchen, cancer, an empty bed. I've got all of the above. Shit.

September 6, 1983

My first payday since radiation treatments in Anchorage on leave without pay. Thank God. I bought groceries today. I also took the article I wrote on the treatments to the newspaper. They took my picture. When it's printed on Friday it will be like being displayed naked on the Chamber of Commerce lawn. This whole town will know my inmost feelings; anyone who didn't know before that I only have one breast will know now. They'll probably look at the picture and try to figure out which one is real.

Isn't something good supposed to happen after you hit bottom? I just keep bouncing.

September 19, 1983

This afternoon I go back to Dr. Carroll and start the chemo again. I may have the flu. I want to crawl under the bed, pull in my favorite afghan, suck my thumb, sleep. That's all. Just sleep.

October 23, 1983

My hair is not only growing back but it's curly! Hell of a way to get a permanent.

November 1, 1983

A year ago I began a new journey — unplanned, unwanted, one way. Cancer. For now it leaves me alone. Beast, did I conquer you? Ah, no, you lurk — you cower (I'm not sure which) — in the corner of my bedroom. No, of my mind. Once in awhile I see the red gleam as you roll your eyes. I hear your scales rub flatly when you shift from foot to foot. Even in the darkness, with no other clues of your presence, I would recognize you. I can feel you. You're there, foul thing, eater of my flesh. But you shall not have me. It's not yet time.

November 18, 1983

Tonight I lie chastely in my big bed, surrounded by pets (Kia the cat, purring and content, and a stuffed puppy and lion, remnants of the hospital), madonnas, books and silence. I seem to be getting the hang of living by myself. I'll be damned. I'm not such bad company.

December 4, 1983

I just pawed through my journal for this past year. Interesting. The insides of my head was a place where monsters lurked and craziness bounced around; where corners got rounded off from pacing; where small defenseless creatures whimpered; where black bats and white doves bounced off each other in alternate darkness and blinding brilliance. It was a place, too, where a birth happened, where a whole woman walked out of the ashes, a phoenix. Oh, I still lack a breast and wear the scar. And it will always hurt. But instead of a resident dragon, I have a mere lizard, a chameleon shuffling in an arid desert. Where once it shook the earth with a stamping foot, it scratches mutely in the dust. At least for now.

It was a reverse birthday, a negative of a happy occasion, everything black where it should be white. I dreaded opening the package for such a long time, pulling a ribbon here, stripping off tape there, leaving it intact. But the time came when I released the last tape, the last paper fell away, the lid lifted and I looked inside, expecting to see the contents of a future coffin, my own remains, devoured and destroyed by cells gone mad.

But the box was empty.

I keep remembering what I read about a medicine woman, who said that nothing, absolutely nothing, has power over you when you have named your own death. Maybe I've learned that one thing, the name of my death, and in sounding that name — in voicing that syllable — it deflated and became powerless.

That hitchhiker I picked up months ago, the one who wore the black monk's robe and grimaced through bared teeth in a skeletal smile? He's gone, too. He left his robe, a grisly reminder that I'll wear it yet. But he doesn't point out intersections to me anymore, or try to get me to take turns onto roads only he can see. I'm no longer obsessed with death; I'm no longer obsessed with living. I just do it.

Melissa

Mary Ann Ewert Borchert

I remember when I was the new kid in school in Illinois and you became my friend.

> I remember when we went on our summer camping trips through high school with "the girls" and you made even the chores seem like fun.

I remember when you went off to a big college and I went off to a small one and we were still good friends.

> I remember when we were in a boat in the middle of a lake in Minnesota when we saw the rain coming toward us and we laughed and laughed because we knew that we were going to get wet.

I remember when I was in your wedding and I was so very happy for you.

> I remember when you had your third child in Washington and I was living in Oregon and we were still good friends.

I remember when you wrote to me that you had cancer and were undergoing chemotherapy and I felt terrible but didn't know what to do to help.

> I remember when your cancer was in remission and you supported your three children by selling real estate in Illinois and I moved farther away, to Alaska.

I remember when you talked about how proud you were of your kids but how worried you were that they had so many adult responsibilities and couldn't really be kids.

I remember when I visited you in the hospital every day I was in town and couldn't tell you how much it meant to me that you were my friend.

I remember when I received the last letter from you, not knowing it was the last, and you said you were so glad I was your friend.

I remember how brave you were.

Now you can't remember any more, but I can, and I do.

Thank you for being you.

Journey

Darlene Pasley

I wanted to go
A chance to say good-bye
I ask myself
What if, her death was unexpected?
You know, the games you play.
Would it be easier
Not to share
For her, or
Me.
Would it be easier,
Not to share
The remnants of
What was left
To say
Or do.
Oh yes, to do.

I read Sheehy and Kubler-Ross
And looked for understanding
And answers,
Listening to the things she said:
    Trying to finish up
    A lifetime
    And "arrangements"
    And family...matters

    And the deafening sound of things unspoken
    About the Real Beginning.

The anger that was silent
When she would not leave the house
When the trap door shut behind her and
She found her life was not working
When her body systems began breaking down
When her sickness began in earnest or
When
The First
The Real
Good-byes were said.

Jessie would go in at night
And curl up next to her
A new life, beginning.
She had more strength,
At five
Than those in the house
At forty. She had more acceptance
Than those of us that questioned.
But she had more love than those of us who
Protected our own emotions.
Who sheltered our own mortality.

I will tell you this
What matters is
What goes before
I saw it in her eyes.
She was alone.

Images in the Sky

Candis Shannon

"I never really thought much about the sky until I moved to Fairbanks, but there seems to be so much more of it here. It can be very beautiful." Those words were spoken by an acquaintance shortly after my arrival in the Interior of Alaska. Fresh from a fishing village where from many a vantage point one could see ocean lapping at a beach dissolving into houses, trees, fresh greenery hiding the biggest salmon-berries I'd ever seen and mountains in the immediate background — all this without so much as turning one's head in either direction — well, Fairbanks seemed so very flat. Now I had been given a different perspective, however, and it stayed with me as I grew to love my new home.

My thoughts turned back to the present as I kicked a stone out of my limp-w-a-l-k, limp-w-a-l-k path through rows of neatly terraced trailers. @#!**#!! I smiled at myself for having mentally borrowed the expletive used in cartoons rather than giving voice to one of the unprintable versions. Quite frankly, the cartoon version expressed my feelings much better. Sigh . . . maybe it's time for a different perspective here as well. I'm in the middle of the Santa Clara Valley. It's certainly very flat. I looked up at what should be a broad expanse of sky. The sky I saw was demarcated by the high walls of the trailer court. It was night, but the clouds pulsated with light, especially in one corner of the park. I mused on that for awhile. It looked like light left over from the sunset, but day's end was long past. If just the glow from city lights, why only in that one area? I stopped my ragged gait and took a deep breath of air. Cool in a crisp way, and relatively clear California winter air. I listened. It was very quiet in my immediate surrounding. The city sounds of cars, airplanes and ambulances were distant, muffled. My imagination moved them over to the area in the sky where the lights bubbled amongst the clouds like a big overturned vat. Yes, that was it. There was a battle going on over there and I had been wounded and brought here to a relatively calm area behind the front lines. I resumed my pace, looking more closely at the tiny yards the trailers clung to. Some were sculpted in intricate detail, some attended to out of a sense of duty, a few forgotten, a microcosm of the suburbia surrounding the court.

I felt my body had been violated, not by war, not even by the Hodgkin's disease that had made a home in my lymph nodes. No, it was the pervasiveness of the radiation treatments, the loss of a perfectly healthy spleen because tests could not rule out the absence of cancer, even the misplaced shot that had given me my temporarily lopsided gait. The doctors, nurses, radiation technicians, the medical facilities, all were given a grade A+ on my part, but the treatment itself was inhumane. Statistically, I had an 80-90 percent chance of recovery with no future relapses. What was going to happen to the feeling something was being taken away that could never be replaced?

I was tired. The radiation to my chest and neck was over, and treatment to the abdomen had begun. The nausea had increased, but was bearable. It was mostly the tiredness, diffused through every cell in my body. About twenty minutes after a session with the linear accelerator, like a wave breaking against rocks at sea, so would the weariness crash against my body, seeping through all the cracks and crevices. The sun could not dry the surface entirely before the next high tide would return, dashing ever more waves against my body, eroding it slowly.

I left the battlefield and went inside. The struggle continued on into my dreams, however, until it too was soaked up by the water, and the sea was smooth and still, the surface barely broken by the tip of a rock.

· · ·

The attendant pushed the wheelchair through the hospital doors and a blast of hot, humid air hit my face, its flowery perfumes greeting my nose. A moment of fear as I was rolled up two planks into the waiting van, and then we were off to the Honolulu airport.

The sky was covered with haze, and it seemed that the sunlight passing through such a filter was lending an unreal and unfocused appearance to the city buildings and tropical vegetation passing by my eyes. The meningitis of the brain had left me with no equilibrium whatsoever, and every jostle of the van sent dizzying confetti loose in my head. Maybe if I close my eyes . . . no, that's worse.

This time my gaze rested upon my ten-month-old daughter. Positioned in the front seat so that she could see me, her face filled with a wide, toothless grin when our eyes met, and her arms and legs kicked in excitement. My precious baby, I've missed you so. As if reading my thoughts, her mouth began to move. I longed to hear her babblewords, but the only sound I could hear anymore was the ever-changing, incessant inner noise, a whooshing that contained bells, trainwhistles, music, even Hawaiian drums. But not my baby's voice. Oh, Carolyn . . . .

· · ·

The once-every-two-month checkup at the oncologist's office was over. No sign of a relapse of the cancer. Just pleurisy. Pleurisy. I still wasn't used to coming down with illnesses that I had to run to the medical dictionary to know what I had. Cured of Hodgkins disease perhaps, but I had to remember my immune system was no longer in pristine condition.

Pleurisy will go away. Deafness won't. My mind began to relive the myriad of thoughts and emotions I had experienced the past year. Pain, hope, denial, belief in full recovery, anguish, praying for healing, doubting God's existence, despair, positive attitude, praying for forgiveness of every sin I could dredge up, questioning, anger, cheerfulness, confidence, insecurity, depression. A musician who no longer hears. What mockery!

I headed out of Fairbanks into the hills. The sky was overcast, making a dark backdrop for the winter landscape. There was an opening in the clouds right where the sun was setting, adding a splotch of brilliant red to the white and gray. My eyes grazed the smooth snow cover of the fields broken tastefully with various sizes of spruce trees, skimmed the forested hills beyond, and then fixed intently on the flattened oval of color just above. The sun itself was not showing. Instead, the dark clouds had parted enough to allow the ruddy flow to seep through from the lighter cumulus in the background. It looked like a mouth. A derisive, leering mouth.

• • •

It was a beautiful afternoon, one of those crystal clear Interior days when even the mundane stood out in bold clarity like a finely detailed etching. I stood still for a moment and enjoyed the flow of sunlight reaching across the road to the houses on the other side. Not full illumination, but streamers highlighting only those elements of the carving the sun so chose.

It had been a good week. I savored the wonder of still playing my oboe and enjoying it, felt the care and friend-

ship of many old and new faces, smiled at the daily ac-
complishments as Carolyn, now a full-fledged toddler,
strove to master her world. A heartfelt gratitude welled
up inside. Thank You, God.

I felt a stirring from some nameless place within.
Overwhelmed with the awareness of His existence, I could
manage nothing except to blink the tears away from my
eyes. Unsure and doubting, I had nevertheless decided to
live by faith, and suddenly the experiment had turned into
reality.

· · ·

In the morning, after dropping a bundled-up baby off
at the babysitters, I headed back towards Fairbanks.
Yesterday's clearness was gone. The temperature had
plunged the previous night to nearly −40° F. The frozen
particles that caused the dense ice fog at these
temperatures in the city were still present enough at this
higher level to soften the edges of the sunrise, the gentle
pink gradually feathering into the night, fading the deep
indigo into a panorama of blues, greens and yellows.

"All you see now are limitations." "You are still
discovering what you can and can't do." Yes, they had
been right. The situation hadn't changed. I had. Now all I
saw were possibilities.

At the bottom of the hill, the fog enveloped the car.
Suddenly the colors were gone, and I strained my eyes to
find a way through the gray denseness. The heater battled
valiantly to keep the cold outside but was fast losing
ground. It did not matter to me. I was warm inside.

Trailing Philadelphia's
Cowgirl Celebrity

Doris Lynch

When I first learned to ride a bicycle
I followed Sally Starr for blocks
down the avenues of Kensington;
tracing that long blonde ponytail
thick as the sun setting over Jersey.
Sally rode 'til her bangles set with the sun.

I wasn't five yet but I wanted to ride a horse
the way Sally did —
hips springing above that mottled roan,
full breasts bobbing —
later I heard
Sally had to give up her steed,
her Wild West show. Breast cancer,
that silent marauder, had claimed one breast . . . .

I think of her now, retired,
Out West somewhere;
Arizona, perhaps, Maricopa County,
riding her proud stallion.
Still feeling that pumping
of two furious pigeons
across her chest;
riding whole again
into that shattering light
which comes just before darkness
covers the Sierra Estrellas with its shroud.

My Mother

April Crosby

November 16, 1979

Mom is having a serious operation Monday. No one seems to know what is wrong. Funny how scary times make priorities clear.

November 18, 1979

Brother Steve says that Dad handles it by keeping busy but his subconscious reveals his distraction: poor driving, loss of memory. Me too. It took three tries to write Mom a get well card without omitting a word. I have boarded the plane to Boston without my wallet.

November 20, 1979

The operation was postponed until next Monday due to complications with Mom's kidneys — they malfunctioned and she gained 20 pounds in three days by retaining fluids. Everyone was scared it meant serious damage to yet another vital organ. The main problem is a blocked duct from the liver through which the bile should drain. Mom too was wondering "what would collapse next." We learned the kidney trouble was a reaction to a test which had required internal dye. Today Mom felt better than the past two days. She looked better than she has since she entered the hospital and it was a happy day. Now concern returns to the initial issues: the severity of the operation itself and what they'll find.

November 25, 1979

We have begun to break down some of the barriers about Mom's illness. We have mentioned the possibility of cancer or even death on the operating table. Mom is so much better. She is stronger. It is so good. I find it hard to be away from the hospital. If my life were in Boston I suppose I could be distracted by it but now I only want to be there with her. There are the things which are important and there are those with whom you can share those things. Nothing else matters.

November 29, 1979

The operation today revealed extensive cancer. Prognosis poor. Two weeks to two years. No No No No No No No No. I can't do anything. I am immobilized.

December 1, 1979

I know that having children must be of this emotional magnitude.

December 4, 1979

I am having to sort out how I feel about death very rapidly to be able to help my mother. "Rage, rage, against the dying of the light," like Thomas? Or, like Huxley, with curiosity, slipping willingly to the other side while his wife reads from the *Tibetan Book of the Dead*? I don't have the facts and I don't know Mother's feelings. I feel such anger with those who treat her with what I perceive to be insensitivity. Kubler-Ross says the ill person must be allowed to set the pace.

December 6, 1979

She ruled out laetrile immediately. We have talked about whether one might go "gracefully," or fight and hope, when the doctors say "incurable" and "9-12 months." Said my mother, "I will not give up hope, if it will help; but I have never approved of thrashing about, seeking miracles, running all over the country." Where is the line between hope and "thrashing about?" We discussed that fighting like mad for short-term goals is an answer. To get home from the hospital. To be strong for Christmas. To be strong through Aunt Mildred's visit. She even mentioned visiting me in Denver next summer. By then sister Becky may be pregnant. I was joyous because I thought the little positive powers might be cummulative. But tonight, since today she had a bad day, I feel so very sad. I have always suspected that the power of my father was largely drawn from my mother, but now I am seeing how *many* people drew power from her.

December 12, 1979

Mom is coming home on Friday after nearly a month in the hospital. All our fingers are crossed. Will something else come up and is it weeks or months or days or years we're talking about?

December 17, 1979

Mom is home! She started crying when she saw the house again and then we all started crying with happiness. We had balloons and cakes and a "WELCOME HOME MOM" banner. All the neighbors knew she was coming home. One sent a bottle of Riunite wine for "reunite-ings." Happy day! Fingers are crossed.

December 18, 1979

But her weight is down to 110. She has lost 24 pounds in 20 days. I have hoped that I could lose the weight instead of her, for her. I have wanted to die instead of her. I have lost 15 pounds.

January 6, 1980

Mom, after having been so much worse, is better. The dehydration which followed bad medical advice about how to get her to eat almost killed her. The first of those bizarre fainting spells happened as I helped her to the bathroom and as she collapsed I thought she had died in my arms. The doctors are hopeful. So are we. But what a rocky road.

January 7, 1980

This is hell. This morning I woke up as if it were a normal day until I realized I was in my sister's bed and remembered why. I pulled the heavy covers over my head wishing it weren't morning and that I didn't have to get up and take care of Mom. I wanted it to all go away. I wanted it never to have happened. I wanted not to have to be here.

January 8, 1980

"If only I may grow: firmer, simpler, quieter, warmer." Dag Hammarskjold. I need a firm, simple, quiet, warm strength.

January 10, 1980

"I feel the capacity to care is what gives life its meaning." Pablo Casals

January 13, 1980

I still pursue ideals but now I call them fantasies and consider them an indulgence. I know that just staying alive and growing are major endeavors which take considerable energy away from what's left for ideals. Sometimes if you're just *alive* you're winning.

January 19, 1980

The prognosis on Mom seems to be back to poor. Her surgery date was November 29; not yet two months ago. It seems like so long. I find it harder to think about her dying when I'm away from her, here in Denver. I miss her passionately.

January 20, 1980

One night I read a good night story to my parents. Mom was restless. While I read I found myself wondering if they were asleep; and wondering how many stories they'd read to me, wondering if I was asleep.

January 21, 1980

Mom is in the hospital again, and I am with her. She has a little bag connected to her by a tiny tube to the liver to drain the bile. I empty the bag and change the dressing on the wound. I cut her toenails and she was embarrassed. "I hate to have you do that, honey," she said. I hugged her. "You must have done it for years for me," I said. She cannot ask for what she needs or wants, I think. That I know of she has not asked for one thing, as help, for getting through this. The other day she came as close as she ever has: she started a conversation by telling me that a man in her church had been sick and while he was in a coma, his friends kept a vigil of reading aloud to him, 24 hours a day. When he came out of the coma there was no brain damage, and the doctors, she said, attributed that partly to the constant reading. "We'll do that for you, Mom. If you go into a coma, there will be someone talking to you 24 hours a day," I promised. And I made a request of her in return. A visiting nurse, early on, had told us that sometimes people can tell when death is getting near, they see it, feel it coming. When she'd left, Mom asked me what I supposed that meant, or would feel like. I reminded her of it now. I said "Mom if you ever feel something like that, if you see death near, call me. I absolutely want to be with you." I have become very greedy about my mother's time and I want every small scrap of it for myself. I am at the hospital each morning when she awakens, not wanting to miss a word. As I brush her hair I ask questions about her childhood, her fantasies, her opinions of life. I know she is dying — we talked about it and she agreed — and she is my source of life. I approach her with delicacy, awe, and great hunger, and I am not disappointed.

January 25, 1980

Do not recite slogans to me, world, when I am empty from my thighs to the top of my brain.

February 3, 1980

I sure wish I had someone to share my life with. The other kids have their husbands/wives, and Dad, too traumatized to admit anything is happening, can't let any support in or out. With me, it feels like it's just me and Mom, and she's dying.

March 15, 1980

I move about like a Martian. It isn't my world; it isn't my way; I relate to nothing.

March 22, 1980

Tonight is difficult because I am packing to go to Michigan while wondering if I should or want to go to Boston instead. Please Mom, *ask* if I can help. You have told me the long nights when you can't sleep are hard and you are afraid but you won't call me for fear of waking me up. The fact that I may be able to return your gifts is one of the most profound things you could give me, Mom. Yet, I am forced to wonder if I have betrayed my mother. The rest of the family seems so convinced she'll get well and they talk to her as if that is so. I feel it is unfair to push her to act that way when she is preparing in the opposite direction. I am trying to be there for her, wherever she is with it all; but am I supporting her passivity? Should I, like the others, urge her to fight? Do I *want* her to die? I am helping her die — is this good or does it show something awful? If there is choice involved, Mom, a choice is your right; and if there is only necessity, I'm trying to be there with you.

April 13, 1980

Mom is even worse. I have kept flowers by her bed this whole time and usually when I help her to the bathroom she stoops to smell them. She also has habitually straightened the throw rug on her bathroom floor with her foot. Today when I helped her to the bathroom she did neither. We are losing more; I am so sad.

April 14, 1980

I am sleeping on a cot in her room at night. Sometimes she can't sleep and I cuddle up to her, her the mother again, her arms around me. "Think of all the years I missed of cuddling with you," I said, thinking of my teenaged years, college, the '60s. "There are times for cuddling and times for not," she answered. "Now is a good time for it."

April 15, 1980

An immobilizing fatigue.

May 2, 1980

My mother is so much in my mind. I fight tears at my desk, in a movie, along the sidewalk. Three nights ago I dreamed a dream of such intensity. Mom was being transported over mountain country, by helicopter ambulance. It was a short trip over green alpine fields, but the helicopter crashed and Mom died. In the dream I cried and screamed and allowed some of the grieving I've not done recently. The way she is facing her death is so remarkable: as she taught us how to live, she is teaching us how to die. She has refused to return to the hospital. She wants to die at home. She will never come back when she dies. No No No. I want her always.

May 7, 1980

I think I'm in a bad way. I want to stay drunk, or asleep, or otherwise senseless.

May 8, 1980

In the airport waiting for a plane to take me back to Mom. She is losing weight and strength rapidly. The family thinks she picks up energy when I am there. On the phone last night she could only whisper and sounded so far away. I was shocked and furious. Why hadn't someone *told* me she could only whisper?

May 13, 1980

Home with Mom. It must be so discouraging to be her. Four good days in a row and then a horrible night of vomiting and a horrible day. She says she feels like she has been throwing up for 6 months straight. She weighs 90 pounds and is tiny, frail like a baby bird. Her dreams are of impotence, and death: one where she had to get a dessert made for company but also a meal for the family. The kitchen was a mess, all the pans were dirty. By the time she decided what to serve the company she realized it was too late to get the dinner. In another, she was again in the kitchen, fixing for a party. She went out on an errand, got lost, and by the time she got back someone had taken over and was successfully hostessing the party in her stead. She whispered to me, "I wish I could just go quietly." I hugged her and said, "You are pretty quiet."

May 18, 1980

I have been away from Mom for three days only but she has lost another five pounds and her strength diminishes rapidly. She is being carried up the stairs by my brothers and father. Becky says she sleeps most of the time and doesn't participate much in conversation, although she hears everything. Steve has decided not to visit me here in Denver because he is afraid to leave.

May 20, 1980

I feel like a being made of sorrow. I wanted to go to Mom this weekend but fear I'll destroy myself. I feel so tired all the time, so oppressed. I need to get outdoors and sleep on the ground for a few days but I can't be away from a telephone. I need a vacation but I owe both jobs so many days already. I am impotent on all counts, most of all with Mom. I need this weekend for myself. I need to sleep. I need to get ready. Mom, Mom, Mom, the time comes when you'll stoop to smell the flowers no more. Individual lives stop.

May 22, 1980

Steve called. "She wants you to come now."

May 27, 1980

Mom died yesterday morning at 9 a.m. I am sitting in her chair. The day before yesterday Steve carried her into the back yard and we sat around her. She wasn't talking and I asked, "Mom, can you hear us?" In her tiny whisper she said, "You bet." When she tired, Steve carried her inside again but first they made a tour of the flower gardens and he told her each thing in bloom. Later that afternoon, I lifted her from her chair to her bed, but she would not be settled. She wanted to sit up, lie down, turn over, sit up; restless, as if she were dodging something. She was agitated. "What's happening, Mom," I asked, "is this something new?" "Yes," she whispered, "this is new." Finally, she slept, and at eight o'clock that night she was hit by a wracking chill which shook her for an hour and a half. We held her and piled on blankets. She spoke only four more things: that she could hear us, that she could see us, and she asked, "Sing me to sleep." We sang church hymns we'd grown up on and the lullabies she'd sung to us, as we sat around her on the bed. After "Silent Night" she whispered, "Nothing more." We were at a loss as to what to do. We held her. It was about ten-thirty at night. I became sick to my stomach and vomited every half hour. Steve developed a fever. Becky, who had returned to New Hampshire, was also sick. While Mom slept, Dad slept beside her. I had stayed away from her for maybe an hour because her pale strained face grabbed my already upset stomach; but suddenly it was the right time and I went to her.

Her breathing was labored, her arm was shaking uncontrollably, her heart raced but produced only a slight pulse. Her face was tense. She looked so tiny, so small, so scared. I cuddled up to her on the bed and put my arms around her.

"We love you, Mom," I said, softly, slowly. "We love you and we'll hold your hands and we'll stay with you and we won't ever leave. We'll stay right here, Mom, and hold you and love you and we won't leave you because you never left us, Mom. You always loved us and you never left us and you took care of us and now we'll take care of you, Mom, because now you need help and you taught us what is really important because you loved us. You took care of us, you were always there Mom; you took care of Dad when he was sick in Pakistan and you took care of me when I was sick there and now we'll help you, Mom. And we'll help Dad, Mom, and we'll help each other because you taught us that family is so important and you taught us how to help each other. So we love you Mom and we'll be here and we won't ever leave and even if you go to sleep it will be okay because we'll be holding you and holding each other so if you want to sleep it's okay, Mom. Because we love you and we're here and we love you and it's okay, Mom. You can sleep if you want to because we love you and it's okay."

I don't know where these words came from but on and on and on I said whatever came to mind, very softly; and she seemed soothed and slept.

We guarded her in shifts through the night. During my morning hours she slept some of the time and during those times, I held her; while she was awake I held her and talked. I talked more about how much we loved her, and about how the birds were singing to her this morning, also taking care of her because she had cared for them. I noticed that her lips were parched from her labored breathing through her mouth and I put some lip salve on them with my little finger. Then I realized she must be thirsty; I brought the juice and the straw but she was too weak to suck the liquid more than half an inch up the straw. I wet the corner of a cloth, talking to her all the time, and put it to her mouth; she pursed her tiny lips and sucked the cloth with the strength of only the smallest of baby animals. Over and over I put the cloth to her lips, soaking it as much as possible, and over and over she sucked, with the tiny strength of a tiny dying woman who was beautiful and who was my mother.

She apparently couldn't move her eyes much because I had to stay propped up on my left elbow to stay within her gaze, and with my right arm I fed her juice from the cloth, all the time talking to her about the birds and about how much we loved her.

She tried to talk, which, looking back, I guess was probably asking for Dad. And she moved her hand next to my shoulder, which perhaps was pulling me in to be closer, but I didn't see these things at the time.

In a few minutes I called Dad because my arms were exhausted. Dad laid down beside her. Twenty-six minutes later, Mom died. Dad knew immediately because her breathing was so labored, and then she was silent. She was in her bed and death came during her sleep as she'd wanted.

In her last days, she had gathered the family. Becky had come repeatedly from New Hampshire, Steve and Jeff were there, and I'd come from Colorado. She had seen the flowerbeds again, and Dad was beside her. And then she died.

Personal Reflections

Alice Oates

Have you ever watched a friend die? I have. My friend found out that she had cancer of the breast. She found it herself, by self-examination. She found a lump. She had one breast removed and was doing fine. Two years passed when she checked and found a lump on her breast.

Her visit to her doctor proved that she had cancer. She called me on the phone to come and see her. I took her a red, ruffled, chiffon nightgown.

I visited her in the hospital and she looked so good and cheerful in that snappy red nightgown. She was sitting up and said she felt fine. She was so brave. She said it was nothing.

She came home and got around fine. She couldn't do what she liked best which was to play her banjo. She was sore under the arms from surgery and couldn't hold the banjo. She was a good player and she told me she used to play in the speakeasies in the "good old days" of Alaska behind curtains so no one could see their faces. She could see the audience but they couldn't see her.

She was getting kind of bitter about life as she lost her boyfriend through this operation as he wanted, she said, "a girl with two bubbies." She started to get thinner and thinner and weaker. She would cook and bake but eat very little. She went to lectures and gave up smoking through these lectures. I would go there and I could smell an odor, "Cancer Odor." I recognized it right away even though it was fifty years since I smelled that odor. My mother had it, a discharge from the vagina. She would tell me everytime I saw her she didn't feel good and had pains.

I told her to go to the doctor. She said, "I don't believe in going to the doctor's for every little pain." I took her to the doctor and she fainted in his office. He ordered her to the hospital for tests and he took the tests from her throat and could tell how far it had spread in her glands. He told her to go home and prepare to die in three months and dispose of her things. What a shock to her and all of us. We knew she was going to die but not so soon.

She hired a nurse to stay with her day and night. The doctor gave her a bottle called "paincocktail." The nurse could tell by how many times she took it when she would die. But she would refuse to take it at times and lived longer. She would take her dog for walks daily until she got so weak she couldn't do that. She could only hold a few spoonsful of water on her stomach daily. She had a living funeral. People came to see her night and day and brought flowers. Plants were sent to her. She was very cheerful and talked to everyone. I finally broke down and cried. She said, "No call for that." I never saw her cry once. She did say she was very bitter and she gave her friends "the needle" saying nasty things now and then to me. She was bitter that she had to die and she said she never wanted to die from cancer. She wanted to die from a heart attack. She had a bad heart. I was there when she told her friend to take her truck out of the yard which she had sold, as she knew she was about to die that night or the next day. She made provisions for her friend to take her dog and left the dog a legacy. She didn't want any church services.

Her sister in the states would call daily and play the piano for her. She used to tell me she hated her sister yet loved her dearly. It didn't make sense to me but she had worked and supported her mother and father whereas this sister didn't. She was bitter that the doctor hadn't gotten out all the cancer cells, which she thought he did. I hope I never see another living funeral like that.

Personal Reflections

Nancy Huxel

It was quite a shock when I discovered a large mass in my tummy. In fact I had to have Bill feel it to be sure it was really there. We both were thinking cancer but neither of us said the dreaded word. Naturally the first step was to go to the doctor immediately. I had had a physical two weeks before so you could see this "thing" was really growing. The doctor suggested either an in- or outpatient visit to the hospital. We chose to have me stay in the hospital for all the tests. The tests were very difficult. They took place for about five days and Bill was right there with me the whole time. He always had complete faith that no matter what I had it was going to turn out all right. I could feel his positiveness and this helped me so. Bill's love and my belief in God got me through my ordeal that week. I truly felt that God had me by the hand and was helping me through my difficulties.

After five days, I hemorrhaged. This came as quite a surprise to me. I had taken my early morning shower and suddenly became violently ill. I rang for the nurse. Thankfully two nurses came to my aid. I vomited a pan full of blood. This frightened me. I asked the practical nurse about so much blood and she said she had never seen so much either. The next move was a *rush* to intensive care. My clothes and all my personal belongings were thrown on my bed and I was hurried off. I cannot praise the nurses in this department enough. Many of them gave me their full attention. At this point they sent for Bill. He came and stood by my bed. He looked so pale and worried but still confident. I felt this confidence but was concerned for him. At this point I knew I was in serious shape. I wasn't panicky but for some reason felt relaxed. I knew I was in God's hands. Meanwhile the nurses were kept very busy with me. They put a hose through my nose, down my throat to my stomach and applied cold liquid to clot the blood. I remember getting very cold but have no idea how long they worked until the hemorrhaging stopped. Then the morning shift arrived. A little red-haired nurse came to my bed, leaned over to within three inches of me and explained she was going to stay right by me all day long. You will never know how comfortable this made me feel. She did stay by me and worked with me all day long. By noon that day the doctor decided he had to have a biopsy. They felt sure it was cancer but didn't know to what it was attached. This was a Friday, and Monday was a holiday. The lab would be closed and the doctors felt treatment should be started. The procedure to get the culture was very uncomfortable and I can recall my dear little nurse cringing but yet comforting me. What a jewel she was. As it happened the diagnosis from the lab was not received until the following Tuesday. The malignant mass was next to my stomach and had permeated my stomach. There was no big dramatic announcement of this from my doctor. To save our lives, Bill and I can't remember their giving us their diagnosis. I guess we knew it was cancer all along and no one denied it.

An oncologist was called in on the case and I was started immediately on chemo. Chemo can affect everyone differently. I wasn't a bit ill after my first treatment but got steadily sicker as the treatments continued. I would plan on being in bed at least for twenty-four hours and would be very sick to my stomach. I dreaded the treatments even though I knew how needed they were. Chemo can also cause many side effects. I lost all my hair, had trouble walking up the stairs, and tired so quickly it was necessary for me to take two naps a day besides my eight hours of sleep at night. You keep telling yourself all these inconveniences are well worth it if the chemo will just destroy the malignancy. I feel truly grateful for all the prayers and concern of my family and friends and so grateful that so much has been learned to help cancer victims.

In a few days I went home from the hospital. I have just had the last of my series of six chemo treatments. The lump is almost gone. Now we shall wait and see. All of my four children have been here to see me. What a joy to see them and feel how much they love me. I am truly a fortunate person having so many love me. At no time was I afraid to die. I don't want to die now but would like to stay with Bill and continue our happy lives together. But if it is God's will that I must go, I hope I go without fear.

In Real Life

Jean Dementi

I have cancer of the liver. Only it's colon cancer; it just transferred over. It's incurable and untreatable. I've had it now for close to four years after a surgery. They said then I had about six months to live; I've declined further treatments and I'm still here. My doctor says he's learned a lot from me, that it doesn't make any sense at all. I guess it doesn't.

What I like to talk about is spiritual healing and life. In order to know about healing you have to know about illness and death. I know a lot about illness and death. I'm 65 years old and was a public health nurse working in villages in Alaska for twenty-four years; now I'm an ordained priest for the Episcopal church, the first woman in Alaska to hold that position. A lot of times I was the only person in the village with any medical knowledge at all and people got to depending on me for both Band-aids and blessings. Even though it was hard there was nothing I would rather have been doing. It seems like I was always headed in that direction, never taking quite the same road in life that everybody else did.

When I was just a kid, twelve years old, in fact, I discovered two things the same year. First, I found my church. Scoff if you will, but the spiritual life has always been the real one for me. As a twelve year old I was asked to sing in a choir in an Episcopal church with a bunch of adult women. I had a pretty good alto voice and loved to sing so I said sure. On Thursday night we rehearsed in somebody's home and Sunday morning they dressed me up in a cassock and surplice and mortar board, and we marched in singing "Jerusalem the Golden," and I was home! They were mostly older women from Canada and England and had as much in common with me as night with day, but I was home. I loved that church from that moment on. The same year I found my profession. In our junior high school we had a public health nurse. Back in those days they were a rare breed. She took me with her on house calls and let me work with her in the dispensary. So I decided I was going to be a public health nurse.

While I toughed out the Depression as an adolescent and teenager I was very fortunate in at least one respect: I did not come from a home where it was assumed that every little girl would one day grow up and get married and have children. I think it's a wonderful thing to grow up and get married and have children, but I think you need options because there are all kinds of little girls. My family was always supportive of my attitude about these things and that was helpful because I thought my nurses' school classmates were balmy! They were getting married right after training, only because there was a rule that you couldn't get married *during* training. I always knew something was going to happen in my life. I had no idea what it was but I found out later a name someone called this kind of living. It's "living on tiptoe." Somehow there's an awareness that life is going to bring something else to you, something besides the usual succession of days spent over dishes and diapers. You don't know what it is for sure but you know it's going to be there. Somehow this was planted in my mind at an early age and I started living on tiptoe then. I didn't want to miss anything. I still don't. I don't have time for tea parties.

You might think that having such a staggering diagnosis and prognosis as incurable cancer would slow someone down or make them depressed. I disagree. As I pointed out before, I know a lot about death because I've watched many die, and I can tell you that it's effortless and beautiful. It's something spontaneous that happens between one breath and the next. It doesn't have to be scary. It's a natural part of life.

A couple of years ago I got a call from someone telling me there was a lady admitted to the hospital who wanted to talk to me. The hospital didn't know anything about her or who she was. I went to see her. She had breast cancer which she had not done anything about and had fulminating cancer rampaging in her. She said, "Sit down, can you hold my hand while we talk?" A couple minutes later her doctor came in, a little queasy when he saw me because doctors don't like to see clergy hanging around their patients. I came back twice more and we talked about death. That's what she really wanted to talk about because she knew she was going to die, she just didn't know how long it would be or how difficult it would be. I was able to tell her, because I've known since I was twenty-nine years old, that when it's time for you to go you can go between one breath and the next. Just close your eyes and go. She refused all treatment, which wouldn't have done anything but extend her misery anyway, and they transferred her to a care home where I visited her twice. The second time she asked if I would take care of things for her when she died because she didn't have people; she would give only "Smith" as a name. No relatives. So I went out to the desk and took care of that. Later on her doctor talked to me. He said, "You know, I just went into her room, and she died. I was in there the hour before and she was sleeping peacefully and when I went in just now she was gone." I said, "Praise the Lord!" He agreed. They couldn't even put anything down on the death certificate that made any sense. But that's the way we're supposed to do it.

When I was twenty-nine I had a good friend who was really into classical music. In fact, he conducted a symphony orchestra in the summers. He had diabetes with a lot of complications. One year I knew he wasn't going to make it into the next summer and he would not conduct his orchestra again; he was too sick. On a Sunday afternoon he called and asked me to come over and spend some time with him. I made him some soup and helped him eat it and we talked companionably for awhile. He was still looking forward to his music. He asked me for a cigarette, I lit it for him and handed it to him. He had died. Quietly, with no grand announcements, no fanfare, nothing. He just went between one breath and the next. I never grieved for him. It was one of the most beautiful and natural things I ever saw.

Since then I've seen a lot more deaths, many related to violence and too many children. The suffering beforehand is what's hard, but I sort of think I was peculiarly equipped to deal with those things because not only was I a nurse and later a deacon and later a priest, I was a woman. It's a wonderful thing to be a woman priest. I said that in a group of Lutheran pastors and got a strange look. One asked, "What do you mean by that?" I said that when I was ordained I thought I would have to overcome some deficiency because I wasn't the same as how priests had always been. I thought I would have to work harder or push more to be what a priest is supposed to be. Then I found out how wonderful it is to be a woman minister. A woman has things to offer from her deepest personality that come naturally, that men just simply for the most part don't have enough of. Some are very much into the feminine side of themselves but a lot aren't. It's sad because they have to struggle through all that lacquer and veneer, all the external stuff that being ordained has meant in the past. For example, at a healing service in a church where I hadn't done such a service before, after praying over a person I hugged him when he stood up. I commented that there was one of the good things about being a woman priest — I could hug people and nobody cared. To be able to hug somebody in a nonthreatening way is so nice. It causes tears sometimes and I don't hug that hard. It's one of the nice things that, as a woman, is there for me to do and is natural.

I have to admit that I have a problem with a lot of women's groups. You get with them, especially in a church, and they start acting proper and their voices get tittery and higher. Don't do it! I'm not Gloria Steinem but you've got what it takes to transform the world. You've got the spirit of God within you and whatever God calls you to do you can do it and you don't have to have fear. You can transform the world around you. It amounts to saying, here I am, Lord. Don't let anybody gag you and don't gag yourself.

Spiritual healing is what I'm about now. Spiritual healing may include a dose for the body but it's mostly for the spirit. I use a healing prayer with certain words at the end, that have a catch: "So that you may love and serve Him now and forever." I really like that word, forever, because I'm in that time frame. The healing is for a purpose — to love and serve the Lord. It's not just to get over your cold or broken leg or cancer or whatever and go tripping around merrily doing your own thing for the rest of your life. It's so that you may love Him and serve Him now and forever. That's very important to understand. I'm not a faith healer. This is a congregational ministry. I wouldn't attempt it without the backing of the congregation. My calling is to help lead a congregation in a healing ministry of benefit to them and to others.

I have a lot of positive things to say about sickness and death. I know that's what's down the road for me. And one of these days I won't wake up and that's going to be great. But I'm not going to die of cancer.

God has been so good to me. He's led me every inch of the way. His spirit, with whom I identify very much — and I believe the female spirit is more appropriate than the male — is such a strong force. If you allow God's spirit to work in your life, with your problems or whatever it is God has given you, good and not so good, you've got a potential for power and grace that no one can ever take away from you. I plead with you to be the wonderful strong people I know you are. The world is going to be transformed more by women's gifts than by any other thing. You know what it is you have; you know what you're capable of. Do it. Just do it.

Visualizing

Nancy van Veenen

*A spkey day The hold Wehce brook her broom. I brook
my broom said the wehce. what will I do said the witch as
she stirred the soup. oh I got it but how do I do it? said
the witch again and again. I (k)now it, I'll do my power,
that's it. I'll do it . . . .*

*Vanessa van Veenen
Nancy's daughter, age 7
October, 1984*

I stood suddenly at the brink.
How did I get HERE?
I came alone
no turning back
time will not
But even in all the suddeness
I felt myself sucking on the seconds as they broke away
wanting them all
not wanting them to run out
I could not go on
This was the edge
The end.
Cancer

I stood wild-eyed
We can cut it off
slice it away
scrape it into a dish
Knik, knik, skrickk . . .

We think we got it all . . .
said Dr. Holden years ago about the tumor on my little
    dog's belly . . .
Dr. Beaupre scraped my teeth
skritttch, crick, crick
their crookedness enhancing the already too numerous
    plack havens
I worried then that he took more than he needed to
more than plack
and missed a lot, too.

An inherent crookedness of my body . . .
A possibility!
lots of nasty little nooks and lurking little crannies
lots of plack missed
lots of CANCER
missed

lots and lots to grow with extra vigor
in my sliced and bleeding
hurting
trembling
beating
flesh

scare-burned
bitter-soured
flesh
Dead
Lock . . . ed

The big hand on the three
The little hand on the six
have stopped
February 18, 1983
The night was long

The knives were sharpened
lay glistening in the dark

it is CANCER

FLAMES roared up from the edge
searing flashing
clutching fistsful of my unbroken breasts
with needle sharp nails
a baby cried
This is my baby who cried.
clutching hungry
fisting angry
for my milk soured now
We have decided finally
hot, unusable forbidden fruit
But if not now
What of his four months of life support on my milk?
nasty nooks
lurking CANCER

We have a night to learn about
    bottles
    rubber nipples
    formula
    tastes
    feelings
Cut off
he is shaking furious
Cut it off
shaking
furious
CANCER

Is there a morning on this edge? . . .

A ringing telephone
a familiar voice said
Come down here
They'll do something different
CANCER Control
and blooming daffodils

I flew
children bobbed after me
breathless, thudding hearts
fuzzy sweetness
half hopeful-smiles
These are my children.
Have they come to the end with me?
they need me
I still feed them
Stop talking and eat.
there must be a way out
they don't see the edge

I arrived in a state of shock
delivered myself without question for CANCER Control
Do it, I said, whatever it is you do.
Deliverance

I can live on seconds
they add up to minutes
a day is a flash
a night is an eternity
a life is an hour
Half an hour
I can brush their hair and hug up their smiles at LEAST.
they love me

they will find another one
love her
test her limits
grow strong and wise on her hours and hours of hugs
They will lick their platters clean.
There is not a woman in the world who can make Erika eat
    green things better than I can
    nor watch over Vanessa's emerging permanent
    teeth as unrelenting as I could
What does she know about the grandfather Hendrik is
    named after?

Who the hell does she think she is anyway coming in here
    like this and taking over my story?
    I am still writing

Vanessa said
a girl in her class
told her
that her mother said
Women die from breast CANCER
Yes.
Some women die from breast cancer
But I am not going to.

Two months into the second half hour
chemo drug treatment
I have lost all my hair
in the shower my children are careful not to look
Vanessa tells me quietly when my scarf is crooked
every two weeks
    blood tests
    Dr. Ragaz
    chemo drug treatment
    nausea

I have an allergic reaction to the anti-nausea drug
    and it is discontinued
Nausea controlled by eating
peanut butter sandwiches
The breast tumor is no longer palpable
The tumor under my arm is gone, too
that one measured ten by twelve centimeters on
    February 22
after one chemo drug treatment it had decreased
two by three centimeters two weeks later
Seconds add up to minutes
while the chemo drugs seek out all the nasty little
    nooks and find all the lurking crannies
and I cook hot dogs
and cut up green things
and spaghetti
and ration the cookies
and peer into mint fresh mouths
and rubber nipples are Old Hat
Three months . . .

Then fifteen daily radiation treatments
    alone on a table
    in a room
    with a machine
    that hovers over the indelible ink X's
    on my breast
    under my arm
    over my shoulder blade
I take these fifteen quiet opportunities to sleep

Three more months of chemo drug treatment
a day is a flash
blood counts go up
and down
pneumonia slows me down

The little hand roves past the seven
I buy more green things
Erika learns to set the table
Vanessa proudly loses another tooth

Hendrik is crawling
the treatment is over
I press hamburger patties
iron head scarves
take my children to a photographer
every photo is perfect
we buy them all
Erika's long planned open heart surgery is this morning
I am too sick to go to the hospital
She thrives
six days later we bring her home
she eats more green things
she grows in minutes
three and a half weeks later she is one and a quarter
     inches taller

Minutes
perhaps a half hour more
after all
a day is a flash
the nights are eternity
Cancer Control
The first five years are the hardest.
waiting
watching
three months
I have hair again
not enough, Erika thinks,
people will see my head
she is proud to show off her scar

three months
six months
a year
two
years

February 11, 1985
blood tests
X-rays
bone scan
Cancer under control
We don't use the word cure here
every nasty little nook?
every
single
cranny?
We don't need to see you again for six months

Three years . . .
four . . .
five . . .
my children will need me
and there will be minutes enough for me
the days will flash
and there will be eternities
I have broken the deadlock
I think so
I do think
so

I was jealous of my friends
        my family
their horizons still dropped over the edge far into the
        deep blue distance

into the unknown
with each step — theirs —
that outer edge kept pace
they did not think about it
nor did I see it in their eyes
my horizon had been brought up under my nose
in one crash
CANCER

and the toes of my shoes
hung out
over the edge
my arms reached back
in damp awkward panic
for a grasp
but there was nothing back there
except me
teetering
What had lain ahead
    and I took for granted
Had toppled over the edge
silently
away
forever

But seconds add up to minutes
I got a toe hold
a ledge
I dare to take a breath
minutes
a quarter of an hour

I stop teetering
my heart settles
but I don't look down
nor up
nor back
I am hanging on
You do what you have to do.

Touched by Cancer

Jannese M. Steige

It has been 18 months now since I was first informed that I had cancer of the thyroid gland, and consequently had it removed. Besides the scar, which runs the width of my neck and is barely visible now, I often have subtle physical reminders of the experience. My tolerence level for foods and other environmental objects has been greatly reduced, for example.

Shortly after my thyroidectomy I experienced allergic reactions to seemingly everything I ate, especially grains, milk products, sugar and carbon monoxide. Since I feel more adjusted now, I question whether the thyroxine I have to take for the rest of my life is actually "masking" these reactions with an unnatural immunity, or if it is actually "controlling" it. I still have a number of unanswered questions within me regarding my cancer, which hopefully will be answered through the course of my life.

Another thing that's apparent to me since my operation is my abrupt decline in sexual energy or drive. I'm still awaiting its return, but in the meantime, that's a part of me that seems "missing." In general, I don't entirely feel I'm back to my "old self" yet either, but as the days and months pass, I'm learning to accept these changes as best I can, and continue to be thankful that it hasn't changed my positive attitude.

I never felt threatened by death from my cancer, even though it was a possibility confronted to me by my doctors. What I did feel though was surprise over how the inside of my body could be infested by a devastating disease, while the only thing I had to show for it on the outside was a small lump in my neck. Otherwise, I couldn't have felt better ! ! !

Sometimes when I think back I wonder what I'd have done if I'd been given — or had taken — more time to decide how I truly wanted to handle the situation. I do believe in alternatives to having operations, but would the alternative possibly only have been a variance of that period of hell in my life? I simply do not know.

Overall, I feel cancer is a very personal thing experienced by those afflicted with it. Although my own experience wasn't particularly a negative one, I did find it trying, especially in the aftermath of two to three months. Of course, I learned some things about myself, and I saw how my "temporary" misfortune affected those close to me — and that hurt the most. But, through it all, I could have never given up; it just wasn't in me to even consider.

My advice to anyone going through such a personal challenge is to cue in on the healing powers of the mind, and let it work with the Divine One above to bring back perfect harmony to mind, soul, body, and spirit. It could turn out to be the most rewarding experience you'll ever have.

The Dissolving Heart
for Betty O.

Cinda Thompson

Two telephones rang and so
The difficulty was in deciding
which one to answer.
But a radio was hidden under the clean socks
And music pranced in and out of the room.
It was the furniture that finally opposed
Softness.

The corners jutted. And her bones.
Her body could no longer rise
To meet them.

"But a daughter, a husband, I am
A family and also I must finish
The course in my chosen school."

A refrigerator full of cracked ice,
A dry tongue, she could no longer speak
But what I heard was:
You walk step by step along a precipice
And it's not jumping, not even falling
When you disappear
You become a cloud. You float free.
Her tears sank back into her face.
"It's the suffering tempts me."

But instead
This woman fed her assignments

Into the word processor.
"See how it spurts out sheet after sheet,
A printer gone wild.
So watch, how I can stoop to pick up
The mess!"

"Tomorrow?" I insist upon continuing
The conversation.
"What about tomorrow?"
My friend had narrowed her eyes to the task
Of not slipping.

What I believe I witnessed was
A human being who determined
She would die trying.

Yes, she answers still.
I believe
We will continue tomorrow.

therapeutikos, 1984

Melanie Verbout

Hodgkin's, stage 4,
Lymphatic system askew.
Needed tests, needless tests,
A sacrificial vein, skulking beneath a Band-Aid.
Tortuous treatments, tormenting,
Guessing and guilt, and
Asking, always asking, "Why?" and "When?"
And "Can't we please postpone it one more week?"

Home from Peoria. Bring him home.
He's asleep. Backseat. Embalmed
By stillness and heat
And modern science.
Then abruptly awake, wrenching forward, head
Dropping. Dishpan waits.

Man-child of mine, with
Cloudy lungs; cancer's cotton in a curled
Fetal ball. Child
On a makeshift bed, straining for breath,
Puffing red. Cry.
Then innocent scents of alfalfa, fresh-cut,
Clover blossoms, bridal wreath and roses, like
Friends wash me clean. Cool hands cup my forehead.
"Go on," I say. "I'll catch up. Tomorrow, maybe,
Not today." Twinge at the incongruity, cringe
At the irony of nature: The now-familiar
Sticky-sweet smells of
Sweat and bile and rubbing alcohol

Intermingling with June's afternoon — cloying
In sunny, honey breezes, breaking
Summer's promise to a tall boy, no more.

Crumpled slouch, dragged, shuffling, quick to bed.
Prop pillows, find a fan, stay with me, stay
With me.
Soon padded, soon pajamaed, sponged, toweled
And ice-watered. Sweat soaks blankets.
Closeness denied. (Outlive the disease, but
what about the cure?)

My son, my own, frame of bones, slipping
Inward. Away. Son missing sun. Again
Nature's loss. Bedroom smells. Pungent walls.
Self, reinstating; body, righting its wrongs;
Nature is balancing, balancing the score. So
Get even. Blot out. Cope. Square off. Fight back.
Kill cells with nitrogen mustard attacks, kill
With vincristine and procarbazine bullets, with
Prednisone poison. Kill
Part of me, too.

Irene

Group Journal

This journal came about through unusual circumstances. At the time our friend Irene became ill and was hospitalized, her family situation was a little unsettled. She needed more support and more people than her immediate family could provide. As a result, twenty women became a support system for her. All of these women were friends of Irene's; some knew each other, and some had never met.

Very soon after Irene entered the hospital we began taking turns staying with her during the day, two hours at a time. Eventually, we started writing notes about what was happening while we were with Irene. Finally, someone suggested that we keep a journal. One woman asked a writer acquaintance for advice. She outlined some journal-writing techniques and advised "At some point you may wish to share these writings with others . . . don't let the eventual audience discourage you from writing. Should you save up your thoughts until you feel confident and in control, you'll lose the insight and vision that make this time so important . . . often you'll feel an insight clearly and powerfully; if you put off writing it down till after dinner, it may well escape." One of her most encouraging statements was "The work you're doing, both with and for Irene and with and for each other (and with and for yourselves) is important work; do make time to record what's happening so that it won't be lost to yourselves and others."

The first journal entry was made less than a month before Irene died. Someone was staying the night with her by then, as well as the daily shifts, as she had become very ill. As we changed shifts we talked quietly in the hall, and as Irene became more ill, a bond grew between us. It was very hard to see our friend dying. We, who had known Irene and been touched by her, turned to each other to share these final days.

Sally

January 19, 1984 Overnight

Awakened at 5 am to the rustling of sheets.

"Please help me" has become "help me" and is now "help."

Someone has left a list on the table:

Sometimes she can't say what she needs . . . it might be:

ice

water

sheet (up/down)

bed (up/down)

oxygen

medication

leg/foot cramp

to be moved up in bed.

I mentally add "sit up" and "go to the bathroom" — though with the catheter, the trip to the bathroom is now not possible and becomes a matter for reassurance and another injection of pain medication.

It seems to have passed the point where it's worth trading off a few extra moments of lucidity for relief from pain/restlessness. It feels uncomfortable to run to the nurse for medication almost every time Irene awakens . . . (figuring out if it's what she needs vs. what I need, i.e. another two hours of sleep!) But once we run through the list of needs, and nothing brings comfort, it's pretty clear that she's in pain and anxiety that only sleep will relieve.

The list was a nice surprise to discover . . . since I'm here alone, it's easy to feel isolated at times. Trying to be attentive, calm, responsive, etc. Carrying on the mental monologue that intense situations like this seem to trigger.

Just knowing that there are twenty other women going through the identical experience helps keep it in perspective. That has been one of the more tangible gifts; I know that whenever any of us meet in the future Irene will be part of the relationship.

It's something to be proud of.

Cindy

You've taught us and shared with us so much. We can't help but carry a part of you within us. Cups of tea, silver.

A Friend

One day last week I sat by the bed watching snowflakes go up instead of down, caught by the currents between the buildings or perhaps some part of the ventilation system.

Today mostly I feel pain and anguish at the whole situation and I want to run away and hide. Later — less anxiety. It is good to sit and be quiet, let those feelings have their place and run their course.

Her hands and forearms, strong and lean (at least the right one — I will remember both that way) a little bony.

Hands that have worked, crafted and created beauty. Strong hands, strong heart.

Sally

January 20, 1984 4:30 P.M.

Irene is asleep. It's 4:30 in the afternoon. I've just had a visit with Kate and Edward who were waiting in the hall when I arrived. Nice kids, glad to see them, bouncing something that looked like gum balls on the shiny hospital floor, talking about dancing and returning to school and having no first-hour class — and checking on their mom before leaving and telling the guy playing ping-pong at the end of the hall that it might be disturbing their mom — would he mind stopping? Glad to be here today and glad to find this book. I hope everyone sees Pat's letter and feels encouraged to write. I've also sent the letter to Bobbie in Vancouver, Martha in NYC, and the family in Texas. I think Pat will guide us when we need it, if we need, and she'll edit, collect, add or subtract if we want to pull something together — as nurse Glenda suggested. I've been shy and reluctant to write myself, but it looks like I'm getting the hang of it this afternoon! A million thoughts and memories and impressions have been mine, sharing this special time with Irene and you, her friends and family. I'm trying to figure out the "essence" of this time, not something I do well because most often experiences remain soft and fuzzy and all-inclusive. However, I think the essence is the power of friendship and the zest for sharing life (of which death is a part). A spotlight comes to mind. These days (and nights) have put a bright light on what it means to be and have a friend (friends, I should say). I don't just yet have words to describe that, but I'm working on it. However, when you find your friend — my friend like Irene — who expresses such zest and eagerness in living, and the people around her show such regard and caring I feel myself strengthened and that I have been taught something very special. (Still a little fuzzy, I see.)

De Anne

6:00-8:00 P.M.

Helping Irene to eat, reminding myself to slow down, be patient. It's the first real time to help feed her. She is at her down speed. I try to slow to be on her level. It reminds me of a movie I saw last week called "David," based on a poem by the Canadian Earle Birney.

David and Earle B. were climbing a mountain when sleet came down, so they hung on the side of the perpendicular mountain by their fingers. Time seemed difficult for Earle Birney but David showed him how to become curious about all that was around them. Rocks, lichens, embedded sea shells. They waited for hours until the sun warmed and dried the sleet from the mountain side.

Small sounds, pumps, pulsing with fluid for Irene. A symphony.

One night last week when the room lights were down and Irene was quietly sleeping the lights outside pulsed around — white, yellow, green. I can't remember the order. But tonight Irene enjoys all the lights on, so the lights outside appear faint or subdued. There is a smell in this room. I smell it when I first enter, a sweet fruity smell. When I'm here for a while I forget the smell until I go outside and the fresh air is a sharp shock. A few days ago the smell followed me as I was driving in to work down the Steese Highway.

The machines in this room look like friendly robot insects standing guard. The one on the left, which is really the TV, looks like a hybrid insect-bird with its head on the end of its wing. The two tall stately pumping machines look like proud storks with one skinny leg, wheel-toes. Or an African princess like the ones I've seen in *National Geographic* — tall straight necks with baskets on their heads.

It's slower now. People talking quieter in the halls. Irene slowly drifting off after eating. Time washes in and out. Last time I was here I was surprised at how young Irene's legs looked. Just like a sixteen-year-old girl.

Sometimes I see the shell. The outside body of Irene. But usually I see the Irene inside. Radiant. Dignified. Intelligent. Sensitive.

Lyric

January 21, 1984 9:00 A.M.

LESSON: "TAKING YOUR OWN ADVICE;
OR
DO THESE BLACK CIRCLES UNDER MY EYES AND THIS INABILITY TO MAKE A DECISION *MEAN* SOMETHING?"

Yes . . . it means that it's time to be guiltlessly, selfishly and unabashedly aggressive about your own health. Time to check it out, get some sleep, and detach from the hospital. Time to take a few deep breaths and a fresh perspective.

It's okay!

Cindy

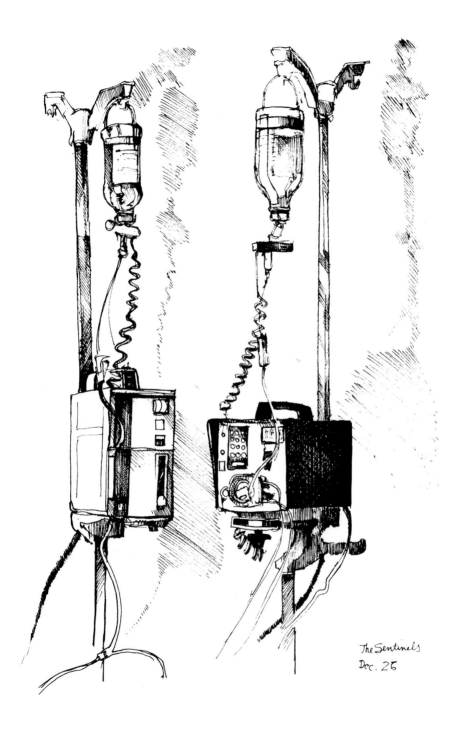

The Sentinels
Dec. 26

12:30 P.M.

I'm glad to write in this journal. I took a course on journal writing last summer and have composed several entries in my head on Irene but not on paper so was thrilled to read Pat's letter. My teacher said that journals are the mapping of the mind, a record of your journey. It has been a real journey being with Irene in the hospital.

I cried that night with Kate when we thought she might not live till morning. So sad to lose a friend. But now she lives in constant pain, and this is far worse. I'm peaceful about it today and can handle speaking to Irene and trying to fill her needs. Wednesday I hid in the corner and wrote letters and prayed she wouldn't wake up. I couldn't face it. Going 10 days without seeing her I was shocked by hair loss and added swelling. But today I smiled when she woke and said, "I've missed you." Her clear, deep blue eyes looked at me and with conviction said, "I've missed you." What a gift she gave me. In her haze of pain she surfaced and responded to my human- ness. That comment helps me know that I am an o.k. visitor and don't just chatter at the wrong times or make her feel uncomfortable.

Irene and I had a friendship that had shades of an older sister/young aunt caste — we talked about love and marriage and jobs and a bit about family but mostly children. Now we finally have a child of our own and I remember her joy at having children and her strong desire to do her best for them. That's what I like best about Irene — she loves to analyze life, people and situa- tions, to keep questioning and keep reading and searching for answers and not be satisfied with the status quo.

"A man's *dream?* must outreach or what's a heaven for!" I hope that's true. God — I hope that's true.

I hate these dumb gurgling machines but then as I

listen they do have a rhythm. I'm still afraid of death but not as much as before this experience. Sometimes when I leave the hospital I just want to run out and grab life. She did. I hope to God her suffering can help the lonely and helpless of the world or it's bloody unfair.

Claire

The Irene that I know — who cares and shares and thinks — reminds me now — as never before — to live each day as completely as I'm able. Even if this means sitting in the middle of the kitchen playing blocks with Ali and Renna and letting all else wait or if it means not letting the little things seem too big . . . This past few months have been difficult for me but then Irene came to the hospital — it really opened my eyes. My discontent was tempered (as well it should be!) and all has bettered since.

When I arrived today I, also, hoped Irene would sleep for fear I wouldn't be able to ascertain her problem of the moment or, if I did, help her with it. However, she did awake, was sick, ate a little, changed positions a lot, and finally slept again — and I did help her! (and that helped me also!)

Thank God that I could.

Barbara

4:40 P.M.

Greeted by daffodils, the room a friendly clutter, Irene asleep. Talking with Barbara does not disturb her — we speak to the essentials and yet there is a bond and intimacy that all of us share with no effort.

Dr. Doolittle comes in. He looks at Irene and at the bottles, says that he won't disturb her. Thank goodness, both for me and her.

It is getting dark outside. The window reflects the white foam cups with straws in them, the orange plastic pitcher supposedly filled with ice water — the machines, the screen by the door.

Irene breathes easily, no oxygen, rustles the sheets, now and then moving her legs. I look up afraid she'll wake up. I want to say for her sake, but truthfully it is for mine. Yesterday I felt I asked too many questions and all the wrong ones, will today be the same?

What *will* we carry with us from all of this? When I see Barbara or Claire or Diane will these days spent together carry into our futures? I think they will. The bond that brings us here day after day is strong and each, in our own way, is strong as well.

Sally

8:15 P.M.

The bustle is dwindling . . . slowly people leave and hush will descend soon. The nurses will stop for coffee and chat before evening rounds. So much of my time has been spent here this year, strangely peaceful, thought provoking and good for me. It takes enormous strength to break the soft bonds a family place around you, to reach out for a single personal action. I'm glad I've been able to do it.

I miss so much sharing a well-turned phrase, logical thought or pungent gibe with Irene. She has a singular sense of language pacing and delivery. I loved to listen to her and mourn her inarticulateness now.

She is such a beautiful woman. This experience has

convinced me that style is a spirit of the personality and does she have it!

I've enjoyed the privacy I've had here with Irene . . . I mean both Brandenberg concerti and daffodils! I used to feel selfish and odd that others visiting were shushed and bustled away, but I no longer think it impolite. The dignity of one's own privacy should be valued and prized.

She awakes — that must be such a lonely experience. I say hi, and the music — that rhythmic cadence and form of the Baroque lull her, soothe her. Together we listen.

New things — the "hmms", only a few sentences, the staff are more watchful, need for painkillers immediately upon waking. I think we should give up meals and ask for a variety of soft stuff to be available up here.

Time to change all the music too . . . fresh stuff, longer playing is possible.

How much more must she endure, it is heart-wrenching.

By the way, spring time daffodils at 30 below are very beautiful!

Kit

January 22, 1984 5:00 P.M.

This blank page is beckoning to me, and although I've brought "work" to do, and *finally* a new magazine is on the table (I've memorized the others) — perhaps it's time for some feelings to be put down. I came in at 4:00 to a sleeping Irene, and hoped she would stay asleep — to save strength for a later time with Kate and Edward, and because it is increasingly difficult to help when she is awake. Her body has become an unsuitable shelter for her soul to live in. I can cope with the outward unpleasantries (sick, smell, etc.), but my non-emotional front is shattered if for a moment I feel I've made it worse in some way. I *know* though, that all of us who have come to the hospital have helped make this experience bearable — both for Irene, the kids, and for ourselves.

No-one in my life had ever died but in the past twelve months my mother, grandfather and uncle have gone. That leaves precious few family and now Irene is going. Is it possible to learn from all this? Is it possible to take time to savour life and to use and appreciate what it gives to me?

I've made a resolution to take these "happier times" that I've fought for from my daily schedule and when this is over to use those hours for me and son, Ian — I hope to remember how precious life is and savour its experiences. How easy it is to become "busy" night and day and miss everything. Irene is still sharing with me, although now I am careful to say little and to save her strength. My best to all of you competent friends. This caregiving time and association with you is personally special to me.

Diane

7:00 P.M.

Irene looks really very pretty tonight. Rather like a young child sleeping. When she woke she struggled to get comfortable. Nurse Buffy helped — on her side "yes/no;" "take a pill;" "no;" I helped her — a cool cloth on forehead — "yes, except it's filling my ear with water," I was reminded at that moment of Claire's wanting so much to know what to do — to make it better for Irene, not worse. Her pain seems so overwhelming and unbearable for her.

I found I felt very angry learning of the new assault on her body — tumor on the bladder. Is there relief?

"Help, help — I hurt" seems an understatement. "You need medication?" "Yes."

Alone — I think it is right for Irene not to be alone, even though it is hard for us to know how to help and it is so hard for her to tell us. How can we be here always? It seems we have our limits. The nurses don't! Thank goodness.

I feel like crying.

I am crying.

Irene wants the door open. Seems nice. Does she enjoy the sounds of living out there? They are friendly sounds. Yellow carnations, a beautiful new bouquet in the room. Soft yellow. Medication — comfortable now.

De Anne

January 23, 1984 1:00 P.M.

I promised myself to keep a log of this experience with Irene and this is my first entry. Irene has been here almost 9 weeks — we have pushed the deadlines back so far they are now meaningless. I get angry with each person who says how much more time? What does the Dr. say? Mike Carroll has quit his guesstimates and I think that's good — Irene doesn't want to die and is going to stick around as long as her spirit holds out over her body. I need to cheer her on when I feel helpless about meeting her needs —

Nine weeks have come and gone. Jessie Jackson freed Goodman, the world kept going and I am frustrated by not being able to share — or knowing what she would like to hear about. Our main focus of late has been her catheter.

Maybe it is not important — my life is making a good right turn moving towards the things that are important — taking care of me — the connections with other women have been a high — quickly we became trusted sisters. A bit jagged — but a beginning.

Michelle

Something new tonight. Irene woke at 2:00 a.m. with undefined needs — when I hesitated (not knowing in my grogginess where to start), she said "guess!" So I ran down the list of guesses until she said yes, and went from there.

At around 5:00, she was awake again, and when we reached another stalemate she said "Play the guessing game." There's something surreal about the fact that she can define the rules with a four-word sentence, and must struggle to say "air" or "sit" or "drink". At another time she would be the *first* to recognize the enigmatic humor; maybe she does even now at some level where pain is not the overwhelming factor. I hope so. I love that in her.

Cindy

January 24, 1984

I'm glad to be able to have these quiet times with Irene. Even though she sleeps or is sick, it makes the turmoil and agonies of my life so trivial. I feel quieted and relieved now when I leave rather than the earlier frustration and depression.

Whew . . . bath, pills, ice, water, bed changed and some tid bits to eat here and there. I've never figured out how people in bed time their requests right after you've gone to do something else.

To whomever brought the daffodils: Irene sat straight up in bed on awakening and said "How beautiful the flowers are!" Thank you from me too.

Kit

January 25, 1984

Saying good-bye is lousy. I finally got up the courage to tell Irene I am leaving when Mary gets here. She was surprised, but didn't say anything more. She seemed very pleased to know that my whole family is making a committed move to Fairbanks in the spring.

I was prepared for some guilt about going — and it's there — everyone that is able to put in time up here makes the burden a bit lighter for everyone else. I'm glad that Turid & Catherine have been able to help. Mayo made a comment awhile back about becoming "addicted to the situation." It's true. The ritual of coming to the hospital has become a constant. Noting the changes, trying to accommodate, and, lately, learning a new language. (Play the guessing game, get the wood away.)

Being able to make a difference for Irene the last six weeks has been more satisfying than any other single effort in the last thirty-three years. And its been her friendship and support that provided the main impetus for some major life-change decisions this year. It will be sad not to be able to share the laughter and frustrations with her.

When I first got here, and the "quality" time was still available, Irene said some things I would like to share.

First she was grateful for the organized care. She said:

"If they had let everyone in who came up to see me, I'd be dead by now!"

She commented (somewhat wryly), that after the first crisis at Thanksgiving — when everyone was madly scrambling to help get her affairs in order — she was thoroughly prepared to go — but no one was quite sure how to deal with her rally — including herself.

One other comment that I have found comforting was this:

I asked her how it felt to be traveling uncharted territory. She said she was scared — and *excited.*

Her courage has lessened my terror at that unknown threshold. I will be going back to my husband, daughter, mother, sister with a more forgiving heart and a greater capacity for voicing my love.

Thank you Irene.

And thank you all. See you soon.

Cindy

January 26, 1984 10:45 A.M.

Hard to write in the journal after just having read it. I feel sad and happy all at once. Glenda just came in and read some of the journal and was rushed out, but will come back and add her own entry I'm sure. How difficult to be a nurse and see this everyday.

Irene doesn't seem to be in as much pain today. They've upped her morphine which seems to have helped. What a restless time she's having. We've had the bed up and down at least ten times in the last hour. I hate that bed control with the down symbol worn off. I'm always afraid that I'll push the wrong one and send Irene flying.

Irene has had me scurrying all over trying to find

yogurt. I did succeed and if she wants more it's in the
fridge, also something different to drink. So far we've
been through water, pear, apricot, grape, water and Tab.
Keep trying!

Jaye

Ever since I first met Irene there has never been a
time when I didn't look forward to sharing an evening, a
meal, a concert, or just anything with her. Even now, even
this, I can't stand to be away, and I can't stand being here,
I can't stand coming even one more time to see this
obscenity, and I can't stand leaving her when my shift is
up and I'm supposed to go to the rest of my life. If I think
of beauty, and gaiety, and laughter — I miss her more
already. If I catch myself not thinking, I'm terrified I might
forget a minute of the times we shared. I can't stand the
hurt sometimes of watching her hurt. I want it to be over,
but I never want it to end. I want to run away, but I can't
bear to leave. I can't bear to see this, but I can't tear my
eyes away. I don't want to lose her, but I can't bear the
cost to her, of her staying.
    What is God's plan; what is his reason? I'm afraid there
is none, or am I afraid there is?

Mayo

January 27, 1984

Someone asked me what I was "up to these days" and I
said Death and Dying. My mother died August 21st, and
my all-time favourite Auntie Lois died 24 hours later. Her
son, my 52-year-old cousin died December 6th and now

there's Irene. My mother worked on needlepoints I had sent for the past 2 or so years. The ones she finished, I put in pillow form and sent to my sisters and father for Christmas. She didn't finish the last two. I work on them while being with Irene — I like the continuity. So does Irene. She met my mother on a very special visit to LaJolla and always asked about her. "How's your mom doing, Fran?" Mom just decided to sleep a little longer that Sunday morning. I know Irene will just want to sleep a little longer one morning soon. Perhaps not until I get the last needlepoint done. When they're done there will be a sweet reminder of two of the best friends I've ever had — Mom and Irene. Boy could we talk, and talk, and talk. I want to talk with them now. Instead, I'll cry.

Fran

It is hard for me to come these days. Too many schedules, too many needs, too many people. I go away next week for eight days. I need that. I'm glad Irene is sleeping now. This is not a good coping day.

Kit

January 28, 1984

How good to read what each of you has written and shared; and how similar our fears, doubts, joys, desires, needs, and limitations have been (and still are!).

For the first time Irene asked me, or rather "told" me, "Feed me!" . . . as though she hasn't the strength nor wanted to even attempt to sit up. The small feeding went well and it's becoming easier for me to drift with and go easy along with Irene's commands, consternations, and callings. She lies there now so dignified and demanding — how I love her strength! While parts of Irene's body appear numb, that stiff, iron bar within her being keeps her constant, courageous, and struggling. Irene, you've given me more than you will or can know. I now know that trying *too hard* doesn't work for me (and others as well I think). Trying too hard to make Irene comfortable, to do and say the right thing when I'm here and to hope I don't get "no's" from Irene when I play the guessing game with her. I'm better now at just "being."

Sheila

I've read and even pondered at some of the feelings I didn't feel: it is expanding. Strangly, after a time, I, too, wished she would sleep — for all the same reasons — I truly felt like saying "I'm glad you woke up while I was here." (no response from her, but that's okay although it didn't used to be . . .)

Nanne

9:47 P.M.

How strange it is to go back and read the things I wrote earlier. Today I feel o.k.; then I didn't — there sure have been lots of ups and downs in all this. I wonder if I'll learn that there are just lots of ups and downs to both life and death. I would like to stop fighting them.

Tonight what concerns me is thinking that I could be saying more to Irene than I am, that even if she doesn't respond, I could say a little bit more than I do, maybe I'm trying too hard . . .

It is wonderful to know all of you.

Sally

FOR IRENE

If I could . . .
I would carry
that now frail body
    quietly and quickly
    from that room . . .
    from that bed
    that wraps you in
    a white and sterile world . . .

to a world of color.

A world of transparent
and opalescent hues . . .
of blues and greens,
of reds and golds.
Where white can float and drift.
Where white can glow,
and light the night.
Where white is cold,
and wet, and bites . . .

Is not a shroud
to catch your feet,
and bind them in its fold.

A Friend

January 29, 1984   8:30 A.M.

Starting at room #425 and coming up the hall are: a woman, 1 year older than Irene and I, dying of emphysema, an acquaintance; then a young man, 23, who has just lost both feet to frostbite; Irene; an elderly woman from Nenana at the end of her days; a woman who needs a respirator to breathe; and so on down the hall. Since Irene has been here a number of people on this hall have come and gone; some like my friend Helen's husband, some like the old man who got well and went to the Pioneer's Home. (Glenda said about the latter: "Sometimes we get them well and send them home.") Thinking about all these others, at times like now, in the hall, when Irene is asleep, gives me an absurd, fleeting thought; "If we could sneak her out of here before she dies, she won't." Is there a little piece in each of our hearts that still wants to believe in magic, that spells can be removed as well as cast?

The Sunday before Irene came here, she and I were to go to hear the Empire Brass. A couple of hours before the concert she called and said she couldn't go, she had a stomach ache, and with Wednesday morning's moving deadline approaching, had too much packing to do to take a break. I gave the concert tickets to a friend and went to help her pack. She and I were down in her studio packing all her art-making stuff — marvelous stuff — all so exotic to me. I asked her over and over "What's this for?" "How do you use this?" She regaled me, with such animation, with all kinds of details of art-making. It was so much fun to share that afternoon and listening to her — really sparkling about things she'd made and was going to make.

She had to stop every now and then and put her hands over her stomach. I asked about it and she said "I think I'm getting an ulcer." I said "Well that wouldn't be too surprising. You're moving; you just went through a divorce; and you're trying to do your job too. Maybe after you move, you can take it a little easier." She said, "Of course it could be more melanoma, too." In my no-nonsense, New England, practical tone, I replied, "You can't live your life being afraid of that. It could be years before that surfaces again." God, what a stupid, uncaring, assinine thing to say.

About halfway through the time we've been here — about 5 or 6 weeks — I felt an enormous sense of gratitude to Irene and God and whatever for all the marvellous insights I was getting about all the mysteries of life and death. Now I can't remember any of it. Maybe they will come back later.

Mayo

(No, Mayo, it wasn't stupid at *that* time. Diane)

No, Mayo, it wasn't "stupid, uncaring, assinine." I think Irene knew very well it could be more melanoma, or so she said on Thanksgiving Day, when she and I noted that it did seem a little dicey to decide it wasn't an ulcer if the medicine didn't work. I'm sure Mike Carroll thought that too. Remember, it was Irene who decided no more surgery when faced with that choice last summer. One of the most difficult things for me, as acquainted as I am with how difficult — truly difficult — it is to make a diagnosis until something goes wrong enough to make clear what is going on — is to recognize this difficulty and reconcile that with the anguish and anger I feel when decisions by Irene, doctors, and us weren't made more quickly with my friend. I almost said weren't made quick enough — but we simply don't know — really don't know — that aspect.

Dammit — we all make decisions — and yes, Mayo — we can't go thru life being afraid of the consequences. But what a fight it is to keep thinking positively about the decisions, and go on finding positive solutions and fight the staring-at-the-wall-paralysis! I'm glad we have friends — Irene, the rest of us — to help with the consequences — that give help as well as accept help. Is it the coffee we need or the friend that goes with it? Love you, Mayo!

There's a half hour left and I can't get myself to start the novel I brought. This book is great: I've had a wall up against thinking about, and to some extent even dealing with, the recent losses in my life — husband, father, Irene for the living ones. I know I have to do something about that wall: this book and caring for Irene especially when she can't respond helps in ways I'm not even sure about.

Today, though — is a day I didn't even want to show my nose for fear Irene will wake, but while watching the eyes open and the brow furrow I wish she would — and she is —

Nanne

3:00 P.M.

Truly what a treasure this book is. Almost every entry sparks a similar chord in me. Yes, I, too dread coming and dread leaving. I, too, feel guilty about spending time here and not meeting other obligations.

Friends ask about Irene. I say she is slowly dying and becoming more like a child in her needs. That's how I know she's worse. In the early weeks she often seemed more concerned about me than about her needs. Is the cycle of life completing itself? If so, why does it take so long?

Hasn't she put in her time? But then why does she have to go so soon?

Like Sally said "Have I said enough?" She sleeps and I hope she's comfortable. But I'm not afraid to help her today. Finally just relaxing and being me has helped me meet her needs. I can't help making mistakes.

Friends say "You're so good to spend time with Irene." I say "No, I'm so lucky I've had this chance and I get to keep coming back." I never knew how to handle myself in a hospital; I never realized you can die with dignity; I never understood dying can have joyous moments. I am grateful. But like Mayo, I'm afraid I may forget these insights.

I'm a baby for pain. How can she be so strong? Does she keep questioning inside herself why this is happening or is she just holding onto a cloud of life?

I'm glad Irene has so many neat friends.

Claire

It's 6:30 and "All Things Considered" has just signed off — I wonder if the banjo playing will wake her up? It feels so peaceful here tonight — no anxiety, just calm — I'm sorry that I can't share my weekend with Irene — that's what I miss — the quick honest laughter or retort — or how she would say "that's smashing" — her eyes lighting up. When she saw Mary yesterday, it was a quick view of the past. She grabbed her hand and smiled, wide.

Mayo, I have never found the right words and this is my second go round — I listen more and search harder but the magic words never come. Last summer Irene and I went for a drive after they found the other lump — she came right from the Dr.'s office to me. I listened, held her, spoke very little and basically froze inside. My mind reached for what could and should be done — I get pragmatic in crises. This journal is great for breast-beating reality checks!

Michelle

8:30 P.M.

I talked with Martha in New York today. She is so saddened at the passing of her friend and longs to be here. As she can't share these quiet (and not so quiet) times she likes to hear about all that we do with Irene, how she is, what's happening, how we are. She sends her love to all the caregivers. We also end up talking about Irene's life in New York — looking for patterns, connections, expressions of life, which seem so free when seen in the light of death. (We said it again: how we are shown so much about living in the presence of dying. I am also learning more about the life of a lovely, special friend. It's a fine story — rich and vibrant and full of struggles and triumphs. I guess it is our story — everyone's story — too.)

I talked with Mary (in Fairbanks!) today, too. I even hope to see her. What a good family! How dear she is to come and make the hard decisions, to take the lead, show the way from here. I feel that I am surrounded by people — that's all of you, friends, and family — who ask the right questions, thoughtfully support one another in the answers and decisions, deal with what has to be done.

Driving over here tonight I felt it less critical, somehow less urgent that I be here. What's different? There is a peaceful quality to Irene's sleeping, the room, to the activities that surround her. Michelle says the morphine dosage is reduced. Is the pain less? What's different? Irene seems much weaker.

"I need to get up." "I need water," "I need the board moved." "I need to take this pillow away." "I need the door open."

Irene said this last phrase several times. I let her know the door to the room was open, I even moved the screen away. She said, "I know, I need the door open." I wish for all the world I knew what she was saying or thinking. Can't I guess? I just stood close by her and quietly hoped that every and any door she wanted open would be opened. This reminded me of a conversation we had one night when Irene repeated "get going." I started right at the bed. "Do you want me to get the bed going up and down, do you want me to go to bed, do you want me to get going out of the room?" These weren't the answers. She just responded "get going." I remember thinking then, too, I hope she can "get going" in whatever way she needs.

Martha and I agreed it would be useful if we all had printers with direct attachment to our brains, then so many of these thoughts and conversations (and insights, Mayo!) could be committed to paper at the touch of a key. Just as I'm sitting here tonight, I remember that I want to write about the visit to the house, the shampoo in the morning midst all those tubes, the first leaving, Kate and Edward the night their mother asked them to come right away.

It is now 10 pm. I'm sitting right next to the bed. Irene has been "awake" and thirsty for the last hour. What do I really know — but it seems she wants company close by right now and likes it when I stroke her forehead or back. I realize no-one in the circle of caregivers is coming to spend the night. But that seems o.k. She is safe. This staff is very attentive. Not surprisingly, just in the middle of this paragraph, the LPN came in to ask how long I was staying and to please let her know when I leave. I will. Goodnight Irene, goodnight friend.

De Anne

January 30, 1984 9:00 A.M.

My son is 5 months old today and I didn't want to leave him this morning since things have been so hectic. But I am glad I'm here. I just finished feeding her. Someday I'll tell Connor about Irene.

Claire

5:00 P.M.

Once, weeks ago, the alarm here went off on the i.v. bottle. Irene woke up from a "restful" sleep, and I felt an idiot for not "doing my job" better. Today the alarm went off. I turned the power off and Irene continued to sleep. Funny that one event seemed so important then. Over time I'm losing my self-criticism and reproachful feelings. Coming to the hospital gives me the opportunity to care for and love my friend. I'm not asking questions such as "Have I said the right thing?" "Have I done it well enough?" Now I'm thinking that I'm lucky to be here with her. Dr. Grauman said we were all "passengers on this ride" — even Irene. No one is really "driving." Of course, God is controlling all.

My time here is the quietest time in my life. In the beginning I had to force myself to stop talking and slow down. Now I greet the contemplative moments. I try to speak to Irene clearly — but say very little in words. We haven't spoken much about death — I don't know much about death. I know it makes me cry — especially when I read or write in this book. Cancer is grisly. But watching Irene transform from herself to this dependent, young child-like state may be more like having your life run full course. She seems ageless to me now. Here we stand in our 30s, 40s, 50s — 80s watching our friend live out her life. She is not unlike someone very old (or very young) in need of constant care. Maybe it makes it easier to say good-bye. I know how hard it was for me to accept it when a good friend was killed overnight. I hope Irene is not conscious (I know she is) of her suffering. Pardon my rambling, friends, but the feelings and thoughts want to come.

What a sad cause it is that has brought us all together.

De Anne

8:00 P.M.

Irene was awake and eating vanilla ice cream with Nanne when I came.

Hospital staff are scrubbing the floors with 1" white suds in the halls and large scrubbing machines crashing back and forth.

She's changed positions several times, is listening to music, and likes the door open. Sits up proudly twice. Looks around and I almost believe she'll get up and walk. But I know how much effort it took.

I read a few entries since I was here last and feel guilty. I feel like I must not love Irene enough or correctly. I see her fighting to live, staying alive (and feeling pain) and wanting to live. So I fight with her. I don't want lack of pain if it means death. And awake that sounds cruel. "I want." "Yes, Irene?" "I want a closet full of pecans."

Irene said she wanted a closet full of pecans.

Fran

January 31, 1984 5:00 P.M.

Coming to a quiet hospital room to see Irene sleeping peacefully certainly puts aside, and puts in its place, all the frantic (and fine) operations of the counseling center. I'm glad for this time. I hope Irene is peaceful. Turid was here before me. She said Irene did not recognize her, asked who she was talking to. Then she (Irene) was hungry. Turid gave her some of the lunch soup and Irene said "This soup is stone cold!" (I hope it is o.k. Turid to tell your stories?) The nurse was telling me there is a gray area between alert and coma. Maybe Irene is there somewhere. Apparently the medication/morphine is up again. Open house at Irene's today. Mary, Kate and Edward doing what they can to move on.

There probably won't be too many more afternoons like this for me. Gray light in the window, dusk, snow blowing lightly, Irene sleeping — I can hear her breathing — the i.v.'s pumping, the oxygen gurgling. It is getting darker, so the lights in the room seem brighter.

Thanks Sally for the article: "God is to be found in the cancer as in everything else."

De Anne

7:00 P.M.

Have any of you ever seen Marcel Marceau do a mime which shows the process of a man's life from birth to death? It is very beautiful. The old man, nearing infirmity and, of course, death, becomes more and more childlike, even infantile, but not for one moment is his humanity or his dignity diminished. The cycle of life is made integral to the meaning of life by Marceau's interpretation — not a travesty as one might think the change from adult to infant might be. Irene reminds me of this. I hope you all might see it someday.

Thanks for the dialogue, folks, I feel close to all of you — I love you and thank you.

Mayo

February 2, 1984

Last Monday I was here for three hours (no one signed up after me). For 3 hours Irene vomited, ate, rolled from side to side, etc., just basically alert and active. That night I had a dream . . . she sat up and vomited, hurt, vomited more. Up came a baseball-size . . . yuck . . . a tumor. All of a sudden the bags started filling up. I buzzed the nurses and they quickly came to empty out the over-flowing bags. Then Irene pulled out all the tubes. Sat on the side of the bed and said, "Well, let's get on with it" . . . and they all lived happily ever after!

Fran

Dec. 25

4:00 P.M.

I felt my heart aching this morning when I woke thinking of the leave taking that is going on this weekend — for Irene's children and her sister to leave and say good-bye and then wait to hear that she has died. What a sad moment, what sad days.

Fran's dream — I love it. I think secretly that is everyone's dream — our dream — and just never dared to dream it. Thanks, Fran.

I brought in today a copy of the *MS Magazine* article about Carol Gilligan which several of us shared — right here in this room last month. I wanted to add it to our collection as a reminder of that special sisterhood we've found coming and going from here and sharing a friendship with Irene.

I'm certainly not much help to Irene today. Just here. She asked for water. I've wondered a lot about cancer — why we get it, how we can *not* get it, what it does, what it is. How fearful it is.

De Anne

From the heart — I wanted to take the time to say "thank you" to everyone connected with Irene's care team. Many of you I have never met, and sure wish I could someday. I have gained courage from knowing that someone is with Irene most all the time — and this gives me the strength I need to help Irene when it's my turn. This crisis is one of the most important things that has ever happened to me; it has forced me into doing quite a bit of reality-testing and value re-organization. And of course, it's terribly frightening . . .

Anyway, thank you care team. I'm very proud to be a small part of you.

Catherine

February 4, 1984   12-2:00 P.M.

I'm now — strangely* — working as the Elementary Art Specialist that was Irene. Everywhere I go people ask about her, children see me come and ask "Where is Mrs. Wickwire?" I tell them she is ill. And they say "what are we doing today?" Life is so busy and unburdensome for most children. Everywhere Irene taught they express their love and concern for her. Her energy was so contagious.

I was just squirting water into her mouth — little bits with long intervals — then Irene raised her hand — pointing — and said "Bugs" "What?" "Bugs." I look at the ceiling and reassured Irene that there are no bugs. Just holes in the ceiling. Then I say "Would you like me to spray more water into your mouth?" Her answer was "More bugs? Definitely not!" I'm not sure if that was Irene joking with me or a confused answer. Think I'll believe it was the first.

*I say strangely because Irene and I spent our teacher in-service days together and talked about teaching together next year. And now — because of this gross cancer Irene is here and I'm at her desk. Still sorting out no-longer-relevant papers.

I did find — amidst lesson plans — a wonderful photo of Irene, her husband, and Kate and Edward so many years ago. I made a poor copy. She had made an enameling (I believe) from it. She loves the picture. So do I. *The smile's great.* A very happy moment . . . contagious . . .

Barbara

5:00 P.M.

Just stared at the family photo for several moments. What promise it shows. What love. I've been down about Irene this week and found it hard to organize my thoughts or even wanting to confront them. I, too, feel terribly sad about the leave taking tonight. The cycle seems to be completing itself but ever so slowly. All I can think of right now is that I hope and pray all those that are dying will have people who love them close at their side as Irene has. It's the least we can do. "Good night, Irene. Good night, Irene. I'll see you in my dreams."

Claire

7:00 P.M.

I heard a wonderful thought today (from a Chinese cooking class on KUAC) and I wish it specially for Kate and Edward.

"May the best days of your life in the past be the worst days of your life to come."

A foot of snow has come down since yesterday. My yard looks like unchartered territory in the Antarctic. Yesterday was not good for me. As I drove away from the hospital, I was stunned to find a 6-ft. bear, wearing a tuxedo and waving to all on Airport Road (at 20° below)! I think it's the absurdity of it all that keeps me going. I hope that when you find yourself "against the wall," a bear in fancy dress will wave to you, too. I wish I could share my "bear" experience with Irene. That's the hardest for me (beyond the wastefulness of her dying) — the inability to share with her and to continue our friendship. You're right, Barbara, the picture is a great favorite — of mine too.

XXX to all.

Diane

February 5, 1984 7:00 P.M.

Irene talked to Martha for over an hour. She really responded at times and it seemed to do them both good. Martha wants Irene to call her anytime. Irene seems down today. I think she takes in more than we realize. But I know that she knows we're all trying our best to meet her needs.

Claire

Last night was one of the most difficult for me. For the first time I felt like crying — the family going — probably will never see them again — they have all been so important and now they are moving on to their new life.

The team remains, cheering — Fran your dream was wonderful.

Michelle

February 6, 1984

My nights have been rather restless these last few days. I know I can fall asleep if I put myself at the beach (where I grew up) but usually I try to stay with my thoughts so my mind can work out the conflict. I was last in on Thursday and since that time Kate, Edward and Mary have gone — a sad farewell gathering, an empty house . . . is it not premature? Then to hear the doctor took Irene off the i.v. and oxygen, is this to starve her, or just to help the natural order of things. June R. just walked in, the first time she's seen Irene. I wonder what's going through her mind as I coolly sit here and write. We all say the end (or is it the beginning) is near and yet the book is steadily filling up for the next week, then the next week, and on and on. Irene's sure a tough cookie. An inspiration to me.

Fran

Irene died early in the evening of February 6, 1984. Sheila was with her and later wrote:

Amongst the myriad of memories about Irene, the most immediate is that of her last two hours. She remained always with dignity, steadfast, strong, and determined. Irene was there until and even after her breathing had stopped. During the last hour when her pulse was less strong, her face was smooth, clear, yet pale. She was not speaking. Yet she so directly communicated to me that she was still there. She held my hand, and one full clear beautiful tear swelled from her left eye and gently dropped upon her face — one million times blessed.

March 14, 1985

It's over thirteen months now since Irene died. I've thought of her often over the past year and the time of her living and dying. The time of my growing, also, as I learned what it can mean to die to the person and those who love them. There are no easy answers, no simple way to explain the pain, the anguish, the questioning of life's meaning. But like all of living, dying has its good times and its bad; its ups and downs, its joys and sorrows. Reading back over the journal entries of last year by the group of women who served as caregivers brought back so many memories. It made me sad that I had forgotten some of those moments. I'm so grateful for having had the chance to share in Irene's last weeks that I had blocked out how hard it was at times to try and feed her or help or watch her suffer. I had forgotten how much I hated to go to her hospital room sometimes and yet how glad I was afterwards no matter how depressed it made me. What I remember now is how lucky I was to learn at a fairly young age what it means to die with dignity and that if I use my inner strength and faith as Irene did I can help myself and those I love to die that same way when the time comes.

Seeing all the caregivers at a reunion meeting last month shocked me. Everyone looked so much healthier and alive. Most of these women I had not known outside of Irene's hospital room and I feel like I must have been observing them through a mask of death. It was as if we didn't dare look too healthy in that room because it would clash with the atmosphere. That's certainly not the tone Irene or her children set but one that I must have conceived as a way of coping.

Everytime I hear of someone dying, especially of an illness, I remember Irene and often recount some part of the experience to those around me. It's a story that needs telling and retelling because it is one our world doesn't hear enough of — loyalty, dignity, strength, faith, laughter, music, art, and, finally acceptance. We only hear of violence and greed; stories which only cause us to die a little inside, not live — as all of us do better now since sharing with Irene.

I wonder what I will remember of Irene's final days five years from now or twenty, but I know that one thread will remain. No matter how tough it gets we as human beings can survive together if we believe in ourselves and the friendship of people. Irene, I hope you rest easy now and in your eternal salvation know how much joy you brought each one of us. I will never forget you.

Claire

Auntie

Karen Kohout

The truth about Auntie, according to her grandniece, Charity, was that she was going straight to Hell. The sole recipient of this gem out of the mouth of a babe was Madeline, Auntie's niece who stood next to the child at the casket bearing Auntie's remains on the day of the reviewal. She supposed it was her own fault for asking.

One of eight children of Madeline's older cousin, Celeste, Charity was known to Madeline chiefly through Auntie's weekly recounting of events at Celeste's home where Auntie had gone each Friday and Saturday to launder and clean. Celeste was "delicate," subject to nervousness. Madeline had marveled that so large a family could afford to pay for domestic help. Since Auntie's only other income was a small annuity, working in the house near where she, her brothers, and sister had grown up, it was a godsend. Auntie might not have done the job, though, if they were not family. She'd loved those kids.

Even had she not seen the child enter the funeral home with Celeste, her husband, and their seven other children, Madeline thought she might still have known Charity from Auntie's fond descriptions. She was a chunky child, a bit large for four. Her pale, angelic face belied a capacity, according to Auntie, for mischief. Auntie would never have said any child was naughty. She had said Charity reminded her of Madeline at the same age. To Madeline, she was a sturdier Celeste.

Charity's gold ringlets had been carefully piled atop her head and secured with a blue ribbon that exactly matched her lace-trimmed velvet dress. "They dress those kids like royalty," Auntie had said of Celeste and her sisters, Uncle Calvin's daughters. Madeline called them "the rabbit relatives." This was with reference to their reproductive proclivities. Auntie and Madeline had pondered how the same convictions that urged unlimited reproduction to the glory of God produced overweight, wan-faced mothers with hair pulled tightly into buns who poured endless money and energy into turning out perfectly appointed, beautifully fashionable children.

The child had stood next to Madeline at the casket for some time, her face pensive, her large blue, generously lashed eyes staring at Auntie. Madeline considered that the girl's view could hardly be much of Auntie since her unblinking eyes were just level with the edge of the casket. "Hello, Charity. I'm your cousin, Madeline, who lived with Auntie." Continuing to stare, Charity acknowledged her with a slight nod. "What are you thinking, Charity?"

Madeline was taken back by the quickness of the child's response, the force and clarity of her voice as she spoke. "I am thinking of how sad it is that Auntie is going to Hell."

"Why, what makes you say that?"

Charity continued to look straight at Auntie for a second, her full lips sucked inward as she shook her head slowly from side to side in apparent inability to understand. "She just wouldn't accept Jesus. And she smoked too much."

· · ·

"Smoking! Hell, smoking's not gonna have a chance to kill me, not with your nagging to compete with," Barry shouted at Madeline. "Haven't you heard about self-fulfilling prophecy? You're the one that's gonna kill me. You and your worrying about me dying. How can I even think about quitting smoking when I gotta worry about you worrying about me dying all the time?"

Madeline sank into a chair. "I'm sorry, Barry. I hadn't thought about that. It's so hard to be rational about . . . There's been so much of it in my family — Uncle Ben, Uncle George, Uncle Bill, and Auntie."

"Right. And you quit smoking right after Auntie died and it was so easy for you. You think I can just up and quit because who can go on doing something that's gonna kill them? It killed my dad too."

"That was liver, not lung."

"So? He drank more that he smoked. It just got to him there first. What about those other uncles of yours and your grandfather? They didn't drink or smoke."

If your vices don't get you, Madeline thought, just living will. Unlike her hard-living, short-lived uncles and Auntie, each of whom had smoked at least two packs of cigarettes a day since their teens, Grandpa, Uncle Sam, and Uncle Calvin had all lived into their sixties or seventies. For all their lack of vices, it got them anyway — stomach cancer.

Barry had a point. One of the things that had made it easy for her to quit smoking after Auntie died was not having anyone nagging her. Her own mother, Auntie's only sister, had told her that trying to quit smoking right after the funeral was not a good idea. "You're asking too much of yourself," she had said. "Wait until this grief and the stress of taking care of Auntie's things have passed some."

She had waited three months, then quit quietly. She kept one open pack in a dresser drawer at home to save herself the embarrassment of having to drive in the middle of the night in her pajamas to buy cigarettes if she just had to have a smoke. At work they asked, "Have you quit smoking?"

"Oh, I'm on a binge," she said. But she had never smoked again, not in ten years.

Still, Barry's smoking terrified her. There had been so much loss, so many deaths of cancer in both of their families. The most recent had been Barry's father, a widower, an alcoholic. Since Barry was the only one of his siblings with no children, he and Madeline had moved in with Papa when he returned home after the surgery that confirmed there was nothing to be done but make his remaining days or weeks or months as comfortable as possible.

As with Auntie, it turned out to be months. What Madeline had been unable to do for Auntie, because she was single and working, she did for Barry's father, quitting her job to be at home with him. She supposed it was better to die at home, near familiar faces and objects. Yet, Auntie had not been allowed to continue smoking in the hospital. At home, Barry's father continued to drink heavily until he went into his final coma. Indeed, the doctor had implied there was no point in denying him at this late date. Before long Papa had stopped eating all together, but still drank a coffee royal for breakfast, highballs for lunch and supper. She balked at fixing these for him once he was unable to make them himself, but Barry prevailed. "Honey, it's all he has left. Please save your high standards for someone who'll benefit."

Now Barry was asking her to control herself again, to shut her mouth, to let him kill himself if he wanted to. Was this her role in life — to stand idly by as those she loved committed themselves to slow, gut-wrenching deaths?

She could almost hear Auntie saying, "Yes, it's that way." Otherwise, she asked herself, was she any different from the rabbit relatives whose religion she had so painfully rejected?

• • •

Inside the church it is warm with the glow of candles and lights, the heavily dressed congregation packed in the pews. The air is filled with the tangy scent of the Christmas tree, the clean wood smell of the simple pews creaking under the weight of the people. From the basement underneath the sanctuary, Madeline, who is four, and the other children can hear the thudding of boot-clad feet above them as parents, grandparents, uncles, aunts, big sisters and brothers assemble in the small church for the annual Christmas program.

Straining with anticipation, the children are herded by as the program begins.

One by one, children rise and climb the three steps to the altar to recite the pieces assigned them in Sunday School. Celeste and her sisters have coached Madeline in memorizing hers. "You'll do just fine," Auntie has said. When her turn comes, Madeline climbs the stairs, turns, and is mute. There is Celeste's youngest brother, Raymond who is just Madeline's age, sitting in the front pew. She cannot resist waving. Her classmates giggle. At last her eyes find Auntie in her mink-trimmed coat seated next to Mother in her black seal-skin. Uncle Calvin's eight older children, Celeste among them, sit a row ahead of them. Madeline focuses on Auntie's softly square face with its rimless spectacles perched on a wide, flaring nose and says her piece perfectly — all four lines.

Auntie, Mother, and several of the younger uncles can no longer follow the narrow path laid down by the Church. Their father, whom they love and whom Auntie has stayed home to care for since Grandma's death, was one of its founders. At four, Madeline cannot know their pain. Uncle Calvin is their oldest brother. He and his family remain among the chosen. It is his daughter, Celeste, four years older than Madeline, who is zealous that her younger cousin not be lost, who brings her to Sunday

School each week. Next to Auntie, Madeline loves Celeste the best of all her mother's kin. Not yet aware of the painful choices to which love will force her, Madeline has longed to please them all. And she has.

Dressed for the cold Minnesota winter evening outside, the congregation remains standing in the aisle of the church and in the rows between the pews. Madeline is squished between the wool and fur of women's coats. Slowly, slowly the line presses toward the door, down the wooden stairs to the table set up in the entry by the women of The Church.

· · ·

"Now what do I do?" Barry asked as he rolled over on his back in bed and placed his hands behind his head. Madeline wrapped her left arm over his chest and nestled her head between his shoulders and biceps.

"What do you mean, what do you do?"

"I always have a cigarette after making love. You're the expert on this. What do you do after sex when you quit smoking?"

"Hmmm." Madeline lifted her head to look at him. "We could talk."

"It figures, When in doubt, talk. What would you like to talk about?"

"Let's see. Money? Religion?"

"How 'bout sex? Tell me about your first sexual experience. Who was it?"

Madeline rolled over onto her back and pulled the covers up under her chin. "Celeste."

"Your cousin?" Barry proped himself up on his left elbow. "How old were you?"

"We were still living in the apartment above the old carriage house at Grandpa's in the city. So I must have been four, maybe five. Before we moved, I spent as much time at Uncle Calvin's a block away as at Grandpa's. But that Sunday Celeste had come home with me after Sunday School. It had to be a Sunday because I was wearing a dress — sitting on Celeste's lap on one of those big old wooden rockers on the proch. We were rocking and singing — maybe a Finnish hymn. Those kids were always trying to teach me Finn.

"My dad came up on the porch and kind of stopped and looked at us before he went in the door. A few minutes later he came to the door and called me inside. He lifted up my dress and slapped me on my bare bottom. I don't know to this day what happened to my panties. I ran crying to Auntie. I remember Grandpa standing in the dining room looking bewildered asking what had happened. No one would tell him. Auntie carried me upstairs to her room and comforted me. My mother must have been talking with Celeste then. Later I overheard Mother telling Auntie about it.

"Mother asked her if she knew what she was doing. Celeste said she was just playing a game. She said Phillip, one of her older brothers, would come into the girls' room every night and get into bed with them and play that game."

"Did your mother tell Uncle Calvin?"

"Of course not. Neither she nor Auntie would have interfered in Uncle Calvin's family that way. But I think his kids' influence over me figured in my parents' decision to move out of the neighborhood, into the suburbs."

"Just because of a little doctor-play?" Barry asked.

"No. It was probably mostly the church thing. You know, I still find those people's holier-than-thou attitude hard to put together with all the mischief they taught me as kids. Like phone games."

"Phone games?"

"Yeah," Madeline laughed. "You call up a store and ask

them if they have tomatoes in the can. When they say yes, you say, 'Well, please flush them. They're starting to stink,' and hang up quick."

"Oh, right. Did you ever do pop on ice?"

"God, yes." Madeline switched to a high-pitched voice. " 'Well, Mom wants you to send him right home.' Click.

"Auntie never told my folks about those games. She knew we used the phone in her bedroom for them — when we weren't going through her handkerchief drawer or clomping around in her high heeled shoes."

"What was the church thing?"

"There was one incident that really got to my folks. I have no memory of it — just Auntie telling me later of how I came home from Sunday School one Sunday morning howling and carrying on. I'd run away from Celeste who was so scared she went home instead of coming after me. Auntie said it took her an hour to calm me down enough to tell her what had happened. The Sunday School teacher had told the class my parents were going to Hell because they didn't belong to The Church." Madeline pulled the covers more snugly up under her chin. "It doesn't seem like such a big deal now, but when you're four . . . Well, like I say. I have no memory of it at all myself. I know I quit going to Sunday School before we moved.

"Afterwards, we still drove in to Grandpa's for Sunday dinner and the holidays. And Auntie continued to be like my second mother. Once I could ride the buses on my own, I spent a lot of time there — especially when I was in junior high school because Auntie let me smoke.

"But from the time we moved, I didn't see much of Uncle Calvin's kids. Celeste seemed to lose interest in me as she grew older. She got married when she was sixteen. When I refused to attend the wedding, my folks assumed it was because I didn't want to set foot in The Church. Twelve-year-olds can be intolerant and I was probably worse than most. But that must have been my first experience with unrequited love. Even in those last years with Auntie, I hated it whenever she'd say what a nice man Celeste's husband was. The last time I saw Celeste was at Auntie's funeral. We never got close enough to speak. Barry?"

Madeline raised her head off the pillow to see that Barry had fallen asleep. "That's what I like about you, Barry," she whispered. "You're such a good listener — just like Auntie."

She lay back on the pillow and pictured Auntie as she was in the years when Madeline had her first teaching job and rented the upstairs from her. Madeline had always regretted that Auntie had not lived to see the Hippies. Not quite brazen enough to go braless, she bought her bras a size large. At home she dressed her boyish shape for comfort. Wearing baggy slacks and a T-shirt, Auntie would relax after a day in her own or someone else's basement laundry or on her knees scrubbing a floor.

Madeline might come home from an evening out to find Auntie asleep on the couch, classical music on the radio or record player; or asleep in her chair in front of the Johnny Carson show. On a table beside her there would always be that pack of Pall Malls and her special, large-capacity, spill-proof, red ashtray.

When Madeline was home in the evening, they'd drink beer and smoke cigarettes together — although Madeline, by this time, preferred filtered menthols in a cigarette holder. They would play Scrabble, usually with Madeline winning. "Good word!" Auntie would congratulate her on a big pointer. "That was a good game," she'd say after Madeline had trounced her.

Sometimes they would just talk. Madeline had always been able to tell Auntie anything without fear of recrimination or anyone else being told. When Auntie talked it was in stories about people in the family — always sympathetic stories that explained away people's shortcomings. Her favorite story about herself was that as a child she'd said "I ain't ever gonna get married and my kids ain't gonna get married either."

"If I'd have had kids," she'd go on to say, "they'd all be bank robbers." It was true, Madeline thought. She let us kids get away with murder. But every kid should have had such an auntie — an auntie who, when you look up after recounting the most exciting development yet in the course of your romance of the century, is snoring peacefully in her chair.

Madeline turned toward Barry who, if he continued his sleep until morning would have survived twenty-four nicotine-free hours for the first time in twenty-five years. She kissed him gently on the forehead before curling up next to him.

• • •

Tubes snake out from needles in the veins of Auntie's arms, from her nostril, from underneath the sheet where it covers her legs. She lies before Madeline and her mother on the hospital bed, eyes closed, all energy focused on taking in and expelling one shallow breath after another.

Six weeks hence, Madeline will receive a copy of the autopsy report. She will never again recall this picture without an awareness of the rapidly expanding mass of cells doubling, redoubling themselves inside Auntie's chest. She has seen its glowingly self-righteous image — a bright white rabbit — on the X-rays, has been told it is an anti-plastic tumor, the fastest growing kind. Its out-of-control growth began in the left lung. Like the porridge of the pot that wouldn't stop, it spilled over into rooms inside Auntie's chest intended for the right lung and other organs until now when there is no room left but that which has held Auntie's heart. It is growing and pushing as innocently as mushrooms ripping up through the moss of a forest floor, like a crowd of college rowdies seeing how many of themselves they can cram into a glass telephone booth before it breaks. It is too late for surgery. Radiation has failed. Chemicals have only succeeded in creating space among the hairs of Auntie's head.

Today, Madeline and her mother have been by Auntie's bedside since early morning when a nurse, a friend of Madeline's, called and said they might want to come now. They wait as Auntie's heart plods on, still resisting.

"Hm-mmph." A throat clears outside the curtained chamber. Uncle Calvin, himself drawn and gray — for he already carries in his belly the spores of a similarly proliferating mass — enters and fills the small space remaining around Auntie's bed. "Could we have a few moments?" Uncle Calvin mouths.

Madeline and her mother rise without words from their chairs on either side of Auntie. They pass Reverend Lahti on their way out through the curtains. He carries a Bible and takes no notice of them.

The two women hover outside the curtain, listening, untrusting. Unable to decipher Uncle Calvin's and the minister's mumblings, they startle at Auntie's voice. "I'm not ready yet!" Peeking between the edges of the curtain, Madeline sees Auntie's head partially raised off the pillow, her eyes open for the first time today, tubes trembling all around her. Her loud, rasping whisper seems to have set the curtains shaking. Uncle Calvin and Reverend Lahti are staring incredulously at Auntie as she lets her head fall back onto the pillow and shuts her eyes.

The two men turn and leave without a word. Madeline and her mother rush to Auntie's side, but she is as remote as before.

The next day Madeline is on the phone talking with Uncle Calvin about the funeral arrangements. As the oldest brother, Uncle Calvin is expected to have some say in the conduct of the funeral. Its location is at issue. "It should be in the church," Uncle Calvin says. "She gave herself to Jesus before she died."

Madeline is shocked. "If you are talking about when you and Pastor Lahti visited Auntie yesterday, I heard her say she was not ready."

. . .

"Where do you think you're going with that ashtray?" Madeline asked Barry one Sunday morning six weeks after he quit smoking. He'd entered the living room where Madeline was reading the newspaper spread out on the carpet. The contents of the large paper grocery sack he carried clanked and clattered as he set it down on the coffee table from where he'd picked up a round red metal ashtray. The ashtray had a stainless steel lid that could be lowered to centrifugally spin debris into its red cannister by pushing down a spring-loaded center shaft topped with a red wooden button.

"Salvation Army. No point in keeping all these white elephants around."

"Not that one," she said, grabbing the red ashtray by its shaft and holding it to her. "This was Auntie's favorite. She carried it all around the house with her for as long as I can remember. We'll keep it around for unenlightened guests and kids. We always liked to push this red button and see the top spin down." Madeline set the ashtray back on the coffee table and demonstrated.

Barry was used to Madeline's protectiveness of objects she'd kept from Auntie's house after she died. While Auntie's other nephews and nieces and surviving brothers had taken paintings, furniture, and heirlooms, Madeline had wanted — and had no competition for — such treasures as unfinished craft projects, chipped everyday dinnerware, the cigar box in which Auntie had kept receipts and coupons . . . . Woe unto the poor unknowing soul who tried to take Auntie's old aluminum coffee pot on a camping trip. Barry set off with his sack toward the bedroom leaving Madeline sitting on the living room floor pushing and spinning the lid of the sacred object.

The truth about Auntie, Madeline was thinking, is that she never really died. Bits and pieces of Auntie — or something so like her as to be indistinguishable — seemed to have expanded and been dispersed among the lives of those touched by her. She often came to both Madeline and her mother in dreams — usually sick, dying perhaps, but never dead. She was still there in the objects she had used daily. There were times when Madeline, never a good loser, would say to Barry, "Good game!" after he'd beat her at Scrabble. It felt like Auntie was inside her, saying it.

Barry returned to the living room, *sans* paper sack, and seated himself on the sofa. "Still thinking of Auntie?" he asked.

"No," she said. "Cancer. Did you ever think of it as being something like love?"

Myself

April Crosby

Note: The passages in italics are taken from my journal. I apparently wrote of my illness infrequently, especially when compared to the rather constant chronicle of my mother's cancer. Most portions below were recollected from memory, two years after the illness.

September 20, 1981

"Phone!" called my housemate. She leaned in the doorway squinting out into the bright, hot, noontime, Colorado sun. I turned down the page on my novel, put the book on the grass, and, sweating like a pig, pulled myself out of the chaise lounge. I didn't bother with the top of my bikini. I rented part of Joyce's house and we lived on a ranch, southeast of Denver. No one could see. I passed Joyce and she peered at me. "What's that on your stomach? A birthmark? It doesn't look very happy."

It didn't feel very happy either. It itched and was extremely sun-sensitive. I was a confirmed sun junkie but I'd always put a very strong block over that spot. It was brown, irregularly shaped, a little smaller than a quarter, and sometimes the skin around it grew pink.

October 15, 1981

The dermatologist said, "I think you will want to have that removed, but its not the sort of thing I do right here in the office. Do you want me to refer you to a regular surgeon or to a plastic surgeon?" My guts tightened and I braced myself. "I want the *best* surgeon," I said.

November 28, 1981

After the examination, Jennings looked at me and said, "You will want to have that removed. We could biopsy it first, but even if it's okay now it could become cancerous. It may be what is called malignant melanoma. If it is, and if it has spread, it can be very dangerous. You can wait a few weeks if you like, but I wouldn't wait for very many months." "Let's schedule it," I said. "I'll worry about the malignancy if and when I know it's there." I can become very logical and cool under pressure. After a childhood which rewarded reserve and 15 years of studying philosophy, that happens.

Late January, 1982

In the out-patient surgery room the nurse gave me a shot which hurt like hell. The brown patch — not a mole because it wasn't raised, it was flush with my skin but not simply just a large freckle, like my many others, either — was on my midriff below my left breast. The anesthetic injection was into the skin layers of my midriff — sensitive skin. I was alone and scared and it hurt.

Jennings was cutting it out. We were discussing ethics since he knew I taught philosophy. Another doctor entered the room (I immediately felt my privacy invaded) and as Jennings cut the hole in me the other doctor related a story of questionable medical judgement on the part of a colleague. He asked Jennings if he should interfere. My mind said "Yes! Challenge him! What's peer review all about, anyway?" My guts felt, "Pay attention to *me*! This out-patient stuff may be small potatoes to you but it's a pretty big deal to me." I said nothing. I felt nothing where he was cutting.

January 30, 1982

I feel like a small and wounded animal. The doctor has operated on my left side and has removed what is or eventually would have become a malignant brown spot. I walk curled over that wound, holding and protecting it, as a small mammal guards a lame paw.

February 4, 1982

For the appointment to hear the result, I took along a friend, Alice. When I'd told the doctor I was bringing a friend, he approved. I approved of his approval. "It is malignant," he said. "I suggest you have it and the area around it removed surgically." I remained calm. I had prepared for this. "I'll get a second opinion," I said as I had tutored myself. "How long do you think I'd need to be in the hospital?" My first concern: how long in the hospital? We all hated hospitals; my brother Jeff can't enter one without getting dizzy and nauseated. "Two to six days. If we need a skin graft, maybe longer. Can you guess where the most frequent cases of malignant melanoma are?" My mind tried to play and Alice entered in, but we couldn't guess. "Australia. Dark-skinned people should live there. The English go there and don't protect themselves from the sun and end up with skin cancers."

"*Six* days!!" I was panicked inside. That was long

enough to die. Six days was serious. It was dying time. Six days of being poked, prodded, awakened; it was very ill; it was time to die. I'd die like my mom had died 18 months before. Sensing my panic, Alice ran to my side at the doctor's table. "April," she said very firmly, "you are not your mother." I cried. "I hate hospitals. They poke you and wake you up and the door's always open and no one knocks. You have no privacy and you're a thing. I won't be there six days." I was terrified.

Jennings was excellent. He was informative and direct. The growth was .35 millimeter and statistically, they had not been known to move until twice that size. "When it moves, where does it move to?" I asked. "The lymph system," he said. The lymph system meant chemotherapy, I thought. Alice had agreed to ask about followup treatments in case I didn't have the nerve to say the words. "Will there be radiation or chemotherapy after the surgery?" she asked. "No. We'll assume it hasn't spread at such a small size. We could biopsy the lymph gland but that's unnecessary at this point." "So supposedly it hasn't moved," I said, my control taking over once again. "How do you know?" "I don't," he answered directly. "We'll remove extra tissue in that direction. Statistically, they move to the nearest lymph gland and they don't cross the body. That's your left armpit."

Alice and I drove to friends, a prearranged deal for even more support for me. We discussed my left side and then turned to our jobs and current events. After a couple of hours Pam looked at me and asked very slowly, "April are you thinking about the cancer?" My tears welled. "Go ahead and cry," said Pam. "It rids the body of excess liquids." I'd heard that line before from her when students cried in her office, and I had to laugh.

February 6, 1982

I awakened this a.m. and the outsides of my fists were black and blue and very sore. For hours last night I pounded my house walls and cried. Very unlike me; I could hardly remember ever having screamed and I know I've never pounded the walls. "Cancer," I kept thinking. "It killed my mother."

What had she done with her rage? One morning in her hospital they'd suggested a drug she recognized from before. It had made her incontinent, the single insult during seven months of dying she couldn't bear. She'd yelled at them. When I arrived that afternoon on one of my frequent visits from Colorado, the first thing she said was, "Did you hear I went crazy this morning?" When I learned the story, I hugged her and applauded. "Good for you, Mom! You've got to fight!" But I see now, in retrospect. Anger is "crazy," as most women have been told; our anger is craziness.

What would I do with my rage? I pounded the walls. A disease ruled. Impotent. I'd never felt the need to maintain health insurance. But I've never felt the freedom to go without it over long periods because family or friends would end up paying so I couldn't make the decision just for myself. Now I was trapped. Betrayed by my body, which I'd always liked. Trapped. The small wound itched and drew attention to itself. Such fury I felt, I didn't sleep for nights. Trapped and fury. I was denying, of course, because the worst that I could think of was that I'd need to maintain health insurance.

February 10, 1982

    Here I sit. The cancer ward. I remember thinking Solzhenitsyn's book is excellent but I can't remember much of it now. But the outline drawn on my stomach for tomorrow is smaller than the one I'd drawn myself with a magic marker last night, and it may develop that I don't have to have a skin graft. And I may be out of here in 2 days instead of 6. I've gotten a single room thinking it will be all I can do to take care of myself, let alone a neighbor's illness. My mother had roommates and I resented them all. I brought in my own flowered pillow cases, my own lamp for the bedside table, my radio so "Morning Edition" will come on like other mornings. A friend came with me when I checked into the hospital. I felt silly asking him to be here but I asked anyway. We had to wait until the room was cleaned, pretending to talk about something besides cancer. Finally settled in, he asked, "Are you okay now?" "Yes." The tears came immediately. "No. I don't want them to cut me." He stayed.

    Lots of friends came as I haven't been shy about asking. Steve came from Boston and delivered gifts from the family: books, pillows, natural-ingredient dried soups and crackers, a teddy bear, cards.

    I keep my room door shut. Think of when you have been in a hospital: are the patient's doors ever shut along those long, ugly walls with the numbered rooms? Never, unless, perhaps, the doctor is there examining or something else horrible is happening. I close my door to protect my privacy. Steve said it seems like a hotel room. The nurses are nonplused. Some knock. Some just make a "click" as they turn the knob. At least I know they are coming. I ate every bit of my dinner. I won't stop eating as my mother did.

8:00 P.M.

The hospital minister came. I told him thanks, I didn't need him, but he stayed. He obviously needed me. He reported on a workshop he'd been to where people learned their own and others' personality styles, and how to minister to each by recognizing personality needs. He babbled on. I'd taken the same test. Why doesn't he recognize my introversion and leave me alone? Anger. Anger. Anger. "I'll call you if I'd like to talk more," I said. Why am I taking care of *him*? I asked myself, angry. Who knows what they'll find tomorrow when they cut? Seems like when they cut they find it has spread all over inside.

10:00 P.M.

I wasn't sleeping. I had a severe back pain. I called the on-call doctor. Young, too young. How can people younger than I am know anything important?

February 11, 1982 1:00 A.M.

I wasn't sleeping. Slipping into my wool robe I entered the quiet night hall and walked to the nurses station, on-cology ward. A very thin woman wearing a wig and too much makeup, especially for the middle of the night in the hospital, was there getting pills. She looked pathetic. I trembled. The nurse gave me sleeping pills.

Later that day

Emerging, vaguely functioning, my hand went first to my inner thighs. No bandages! No skin graft! I celebrated inside. Determinedly, next I felt my left side. Big bandages. I went under again. He had also cut three other spots, possible, potential cancers, while I was out. I had four wounds. All over I was cut up.

February 17, 1982

The first time I started to change the dressing on my wound everything was dried on and it all stuck as I pulled. It hurt. Feeling silly, I realized if I wet everything, it would pull off without hurting. Still, it was awkward. If I changed the bandage standing up, everything fell off before I could get it taped down. If I did it lying down, I couldn't see what I was doing. I had large metal staples in me, all in a row for seven inches. It looked like little railroad tracks.

February 25, 1982

I wonder if they got it all. I'm doing better. I wonder if there are little cancers all over me. My freckles itch with fear. Steve writes that his do too, and all my friends are arranging to have their moles removed as they've been meaning to do for years. I wonder if they got it all. My body feels apart from me; an object, not me. I wonder if they got it all. Sometimes my left armpit aches with fear.

March 1, 1982

I went back to the doctor because it seemed to me the stitches weren't healing right. "They're okay," he said, peering at them. "But one of the places we biopsied needs more extensive surgery. The cells from your arm contained precancerous nuclei." Precancerous nuclei? I envisioned Shiva, with her arms of destruction and reproduction dancing in my cells. Seductive, evil, wreaking havoc; the cancer goddess. I didn't have much time to prepare, preferable for an introvert. He numbed my upper right arm and cut out another two or three inches. I was shaken with the cancer fear: they found more; they will always find more; they'll keep cutting more; it won't end; my body is besieged. I felt like I'd just gotten back up to my knees and someone knocked me down again.

March 2, 1982

My body heals more slowly than I'd expected (always invincible) but my psyche is the real enigma. I have a version of the disease that killed my mother and my rage at it — and my fear of it — are totally overwhelming. I am out of control.

March 4, 1982

Two violent dreams since the operation: walking through my Massachusetts neighborhood; spring day and flower-gazing; visiting with neighbors who work on their lawns. A friend's mother, a neighborhood matron, invites me in and she also introduces me to a blind, rather ethereal girl, maybe an American Friends Service exchange student. (Shiva?) We sit down to dinner amidst soft candlelight which rapidly becomes sinister and the candles are sources of evil energy. The blind girl floats out of the room as if on roller skates, and my friend's mother becomes an iron fire-poker with the lower end resting on the dining room chair and the upper end leaning forward against the table, glowing white hot. The other dream: I am visiting some rather tough women; tough but nice, like the Hell's Angels woman who lived in the apartment beneath mine in Colorado during college. We are in a dirty, uncared for, isolated cabin, itself not threatening, talking. I don't know them especially. Their men appear and are threatening. The women gather around to protect me but I am on my back on the floor and the men dump slowly, onto my stomach and chest, a mutilated bloody loon.

March 12, 1982

I feel like myself again! I am happy, strong, powerful, well! Such a relief! Such gratitude! Such energy!

March 14, 1982

Now that I am stronger I can say that what was especially horrible was that I might die. Perhaps I would be like my mother. Was there anything in me that wanted to die? As it took so long for me to heal and become myself again, I wondered if my psyche as well as my body had betrayed me and I didn't want to heal and would die.

May 19, 1982

I enjoy keeping my scrapbook but I cannot bring myself to put my mother's photographs and letters in it. I can finger things of hers without tears but I cannot paste the remnants in a scrapbook. It would be too final.

May 27, 1982

> *When I picked out the jungle*
> *to learn how to be,*
> *leaf by leaf,*
> *I went on with my lessons*
> *and learned to be root, deep*
>   *clay,*
> *voiceless earth, transparent*
>   *night,*
> *and beyond that, bit by bit,*
>   *the whole jungle.*
>   *— Pablo Neruda*

I am feeling stronger, like myself, like jungle roots.

June 14, 1982

I read about sunburn and skin cancer in Newsweek *today and one line read, "the most lethal and rarest kind of serious skin cancer, malignant melanoma . . . . " and it chilled me to the bone. I have to go for regular checks for five years. Tonight I found myself thinking that sometimes life just wears me out, and with a jolt I wondered if that was passive thinking indicating a lessening desire to live. The desire to* live is very important to those fighting serious illness. I want to get strong and feel strong and be strong.

June 23, 1982

Today is a happy day. Yesterday I turned my hair to curls and I feel lightheaded and lighthearted. Even more enlightening were Jennings' words of assurance that no more cancer signs appear.

June 30, 1982

Getting stronger, getting stronger; the "Rocky" theme song runs through my brain and I laugh because I know Becky cleans house to that music. This is me again.

July 10, 1982

Like him you want to call forth a still
      invisible mate
A silent listener in whom a reply slowly
      awakens
Warming itself by hearing yours to become
Your own bold feelings blazing partner.
                    — Rilke

My own bold feelings are back (still no blazing partner); I am in my body. I am strong like tall trees and tall grasses; I have wholeness, my immortality back.

Conjuring Borealis

Doris Lynch

Outside your gabled window, wind
unravels the slender petioles of leaves.
Apple trees now heavy with fruit
balance over the goldenrod of pastures.

You are getting ready to leave this life.
Looking down at the cancerous swell
that is your body: "My neighbors will no longer
drink from my cups. Am I such a leper?"
you say over the ten-second delay,
the thousands of miles
of telephone wires and satellites.

I can not let you go —
even these thousands of miles away
I can not let you go. Still,
I can not grant you stay.

These mountains here,
numerous as Pennsylvania fenceposts,
might I mold from them their firmness,
make whole again those melons on your chest.

And later, when night bandages the sky
with layers of black gauze, delicate as bridal lace,
I will bundle fire and magic;
scrape this Northern sky
clean of its Borealis skin

and bring you suitcased in the metal slot of aeroplanes
this dance, this spray of night sky
to lighten up your journey.

Acknowledgments

Vanessapress appreciates the support of the following individuals and businesses. Their generous contributions of time, energy and money made publication of this collection possible.

Alaska Energy Corporation
A Moveable Feast
An Anonymous Friend
Jean Anderson
Marvin Anderson
Terry Anderson
Bear and Seal Restaurant
B J's Deli
Black Angus Restaurant
Willie Bliss
Mary Ann Borchert
Gina Brennan
Barbara Bruno
Cafe de Paris
Sharon Carter
Karen Cedzo
Chaparall
Jan Sanders & Robert Chapman
Chuck E Cheese
Claudio's
Clinkerdagger's
Club Eleven
College Floral
Donald J. Cook
Jolana Cook
Karen Covino
Stephen P. Crosby
Cathryn Cunningham
Debbie Davis-Van Stone
Sue M. Dean
Betty Fulton Dent
Clarice Dukeminier
Fairbanks Bakery
Sharon Faverty

Flannigan's
Janice Glenn
Carol Gold
Dean & Sheila Gottehrer
Judith Gumm
Laurel Haas
Adelaide Hanneman
De Anne Haseltine
Merritt Helfferich
Hunan Garden
Ivory Jack's
Connie Johnson
Monte Jordon
Paul Jordon
Patricia Joy
Patty Kastelic
Kentucky Fried Chicken
Gene Kingrea
Louise Kowalski
Jacqueline LaPerriere
Beth Laursen
Los Amigos
Mariann Loveland
Kathy Marchlinski
Melanie Marotta
Sherry Modrow
Richard Moranec
Susan McInnis
M. E. Moran
Gretchen Murphy
Helen Myers
Ralph Nestor
Patrick O'Brien
Janet O'Dowd

Connie Olson
Patrick O'Rourke
Linda Patton
Alan Paulson
Irene Peyton
William Phillips
Charla Ranch
Ranch Dinner House
Frances Reed
Royal Fork
Turid & Ron Senungetuk
Diane Shaw
Sue Sheriff
Debra Shugert
Jamelia Saied
Melissa Simpson
Peter Simpson
Riki Sipe
Spirit Mountain Press
Jackie Stormer
Kemble & Mildred Stout

Constance Stricks
Sunset Strip
Fran Tannian
Joyce A. Taylor
Valerie Therrien
Cinda Thompson
Jean & Bob Tsigonis
Turtle Club
Danetta Wakefield
Helen Walker
Carolyne Wallace
Patricia Walsh
B. J. Webb
Judith Weeden
Jo Wenger
Margery Wienbar
Wild Iris Cafe
Josie Wooding
Kay Workman
M. Jeanne Yoder